BACH

for All Seasons

CHOIRBOOK

AUGSBURG FORTRESS
MINNEAPOLIS

Bach for All Seasons
Choirbook

Contributing editors: Richard Erickson, Mark Bighley
Editors: Carol Carver, Ryan French, Martin A. Seltz, Christopher Sidorfsky, Frank Stoldt, Eric Vollen
Music engraving: Thomas Schaller, Mensura Music Preparation
Cover design: Lecy Design

The paper used in this publication meets the minimum requirements of the American National Standard for Information Sciences—Permanence of Paper for Printed Materials, ANSI Z39.48-1984.
Printed in the United States of America.

ISBN 0-8006-5854-X
12-5854

04 03 5 6

CONTENTS

Introduction		iv
Performance Notes		vi
Savior of the Nations, Come (chorale)	*Nun komm, der Heiden Heiland*	1
Savior of the Nations, Come	*Nun komm, der Heiden Heiland*	2
Wake, Awake, for Night Is Flying (chorale)	*Gloria sei dir gesungen*	14
Zion Hears the Watchmen Singing	*Zion hört die Wächter singen*	16
Gloria in excelsis Deo	*Gloria in excelsis Deo*	22
From Heaven Above to Earth I Come	*Vom Himmel hoch, da komm ich her*	26
From Heaven Above to Earth I Come (chorale)	*Ach mein herzliebes Jesulein*	33
O Morning Star, How Fair and Bright! (chorale)	*Wie bin ich doch so herzlich froh*	34
Break Forth, O Beauteous Heavenly Light (chorale)	*Brich an, o schönes Morgenlicht*	36
Bring Low Our Ancient Adam	*Ertöt uns durch dein Güte*	37
The Only Son from Heaven	*Herr Christ, der einig Gotts Sohn*	37
Transcendent, Holy God	*Dem wir das Heilig itzt*	44
All Creatures Great and Small (chorale)	*Gelobet sei der Herr*	48
Jesus, My Sweet Pleasure (chorales)	*Jesu, meine Freude*	49
O Sacred Head, Now Wounded (chorale)	*O Haupt voll Blut und Wunden*	61
Crucifixus	*Crucifixus*	62
Christ Is Arisen (chorale)	*Christ ist erstanden*	69
Lord Jesus Christ, God's Only Son	*Jesus Christus, Gottes Sohn*	74
Christ Jesus Lay in Death's Strong Bands (chorale)	*Wir essen und leben wohl*	79
Come, Holy Ghost, God and Lord (chorale)	*Du heilige Brunst, süßer Trost*	80
Lord, Keep Us Steadfast in Your Word (chorale)	*Erhalt uns, Herr, bei deinem Wort*	82
A Mighty Fortress Is Our God (chorale)	*Ein feste Burg ist unser Gott*	83
Lord, Thee I Love with All My Heart (chorale)	*Ach Herr, laß dein lieb Engelein*	84
O Jesus Christ, My Life, My Light	*O Jesu Christ, meins Lebens Licht*	86
Alleluia	*Alleluia*	96
Jesu, Joy—My Joy Forever	*Jesus bleibet meine Freude*	103
Jesu, Joy of My Desiring	*Wohl mir, daß ich Jesum habe*	103
Now Thank We All Our God	*Nun danket alle Gott*	112
Now Thank We All Our God (chorale)	*Nun danket alle Gott*	117
What God Ordains Is Good Indeed	*Was Gott tut, das ist wohlgetan*	118
What God Ordains Is Good Indeed (chorale)	*Was Gott tut, das ist wohlgetan*	123
Salvation unto Us Has Come (chorale)	*Es ist das Heil uns kommen her*	124
All Who Believe and Are Baptized (chorale)		125
Now All the Woods Are Sleeping (chorale)	*Nun ruhen alle Wälder*	126
O Bread of Life from Heaven (chorale)		127
Kyrie! God, Father in Heaven Above (chorale)	*Kyrie, Gott Vater in Ewigkeit*	128
All Glory Be to God on High (chorale)	*Allein Gott in der Höh sei Ehr*	135
We All Believe in One True God (chorale)	*Wir glauben all an einen Gott*	136
Holy, Holy, Holy (chorale)	*Sanctus*	142
O Lamb of God Most Holy (chorale)	*O Lamm Gottes, unschuldig*	143
Dona nobis pacem	*Dona nobis pacem*	144
Gloria in excelsis Deo (C instrument)		154
Acknowledgments		155
Indexes		157

INTRODUCTION

The Christian faith has produced thousands of musicians whose gifts and vision have enriched the church's worship in various times and places. Some would suggest that Johann Sebastian Bach (1685–1750) marks a pinnacle of musical and theological achievement rarely witnessed in the history of the church. On the 250th anniversary of his death it is fitting to honor the life, death, and musical achievements of this great musician. For this reason *Bach for All Seasons* has been prepared.

BACH'S LIFE

Throughout his life, Bach was an active musician and composer for the church as well as the royal court in various German cities. As a young man in Arnstadt (1704–1707), Mühlhausen (1707–1708), and Weimar (1708–1717), Bach's energies primarily were focused on the organ and its music. From these years come the majority of his famous organ works that still form the basis of modern organ repertoire. A body of early cantatas was also composed during these years. Between 1717–1723, Bach lived and worked in the Reformed royal court at Cöthen, where many of his compositions for solo instrument, harpsichord, and chamber ensemble were created.

After 1723 and up to his death, Bach lived in Leipzig, where his work revolved around music for the church, the town's various musical societies, and teaching Latin to school boys. This period witnessed the composition of hundreds of church cantatas (or *Hauptmusik* as liturgical sources often refer to these works), the large passions, the *Christmas Oratorio*, the Mass in B Minor, and various other major and minor works for voices and instruments. Regardless of the context in which Bach worked, his compositions are marked by the synthesis of various baroque musical forms and styles, Lutheran theology, highly developed musical rhetoric, and the texts and tunes of the congregational chorale.

THIS COLLECTION

Bach for All Seasons is a representative sampling of Bach's choral music designed for use by present-day choirs. Included is material that can be sung within the contemporary context of worship throughout the entirety of the church year, as well as in concert. Special emphasis has been placed on music that can form the basis of a church choir's repertoire over the course of several years.

In this collection are a variety of selections from the close to 200 extant church cantatas, as well as the *Magnificat*, the Mass in B Minor, and the St. John and St. Matthew passions. Alongside these larger movements are a selection of harmonized chorale melodies that reflect the German Lutheran tradition in which Bach primarily worked. The earliest work included in this collection dates from ca. 1707 ("Lord Jesus Christ, God's Only Son" from *Christ lag in Todesbanden*); the latest date from ca. 1747 ("Crucifixus" and "Dona nobis pacem" from Mass in B Minor).

EDITORIAL PRINCIPLES

Several principles guided the preparation of this volume. The historical significance of the composer's choral music is reflected by the various selections that have been included. Chorale harmonizations, fugues, French overtures, *stile antico* counterpoint, and chorale fantasias represent Bach's mastery of the variety of musical forms available to him.

A contemporary concern for the pastoral usefulness of Bach's music suggested the inclusion of material that is congruent with current theological, homiletical, and sacramental emphases. Because the Lutheran tradition in which Bach lived and worked understands music to be the *viva vox evangelii* (the living voice of the gospel), this collection was designed to support the church's ministry of proclamation through word and sacrament for the present age. Care was taken to avoid archaic or offensive theology and language that is problematic for today's worshiper.

Selections were also chosen to support liturgical usage throughout the entire year within the context of the service of Holy Communion. Because the cantatas were written to be sung in the context of the weekly eucharistic assembly, references to the sacramental meal (*Abendmahl*, *Mahl der Hochzeit*, *Osterfladen*, and so forth) abound in the texts. Singing selected movements during the distribution of communion is one practice that can assist the listener to recognize the sacramental references. A comprehensive set of lectionary and topical indexes is included at the conclusion of the volume. These will assist choirs in singing Bach's music throughout the changing seasons of the church year, as well as at the services of baptism, marriage, and burial.

Finally, the desire for the music's accessibility by parish choirs required that choices provide both a sense of achievement and challenge. Choirs with very limited resources can sing simple four-part chorale harmonizations. More complex movements are included in order to provide choirs the opportunity to sing more ambitious excerpts.

TEXTS

The text for each movement is included in the original Latin or German version, and, in most cases, is supported by one or two English translations suitable for singing. German texts generally have been edited for grammar and style in accordance to *Evangelisches Gesangbuch* (1989), the most recent chorale book of Lutheran churches in Germany.

English texts were newly prepared or chosen from existing translations based on the following criteria: faithfulness to the original German or Latin text, congruence with a North American congregation's memory of singing the chorales in English, lyricism of the English poetry, the worldview of the contemporary theological mind, and the musical demands of Bach's compositional structures.

KEYBOARD SCORES

A keyboard accompaniment for each selection has been newly prepared. In each case, the accompaniment is designed as a reduction of Bach's original instrumental scoring. It simultaneously provides careful support for the choir and remains idiomatic to the keyboard. Each selection may be supported by keyboard alone, although the addition of obbligato instruments supported by continuo will greatly enrich performance. Scores and orchestral parts are available in a variety of library editions (*Bach Gesellschaft* [BG], *Neue Bach-Ausgabe* [NBA], and so forth) as well as from various publishers of performing editions.

RECORDING

A recording of selections from *Bach for All Seasons* is available. Supported by the generosity of the Lutheran Brotherhood Foundation, a compact disc of the Holy Trinity Bach Choir under the direction of Richard Erickson provides a sampling of this collection.

FOR FURTHER READING

Boyd, Malcom, and John Butt, eds. *J. S. Bach (Oxford Composer Companions)*. New York: Oxford University Press, 1999.

Butt, John. *The Sacred Choral Music of J. S. Bach: A Handbook*. Orleans, MA: Paraclete Press, 1997.

Daw, Stephen. *The Music of Johann Sebastian Bach: The Choral Works*. Rutherford: Fairleigh Dickenson University Press, 1981.

Pelikan, Jaroslav. *Bach among the Theologians*. Philadelphia: Fortress Press, 1986.

Rilling, Helmut. *The Texts to Johann Sebastian Bach's Church Cantatas*. Tr. Z. Philip Ambrose. Neuhausen-Stuttgart: Hänssler-Verlag, 1984.

Stiller, Günther. *Johann Sebastian Bach and Liturgical Life in Leipzig*. English translation edited by Robin Leaver. St. Louis: Concordia Publishing House, 1984.

Whittaker, W. Gillies. *The Cantatas of Johann Sebastian Bach*. 2 vols. New York: Oxford University Press, 1959.

Wolff, Christoph, ed. *The World of the Bach Cantatas*. 1 vol to date. New York: W. W. Norton, 1997–.

PERFORMANCE NOTES

Our hope is that many singers, instrumentalists, and hearers will be enriched by the use of this book. While none of the pieces included in this collection require a large choir, they do include a wide range of difficulty levels. Directors, therefore, will need to employ careful judgment in choosing works best suited to a particular choir.

SINGERS

While Bach sung in German or Latin might be preferable from a stylistic and musical standpoint, it is perhaps not always the best liturgical or practical choice. For that reason, and in order to encourage more singing of Bach's music within the present-day liturgical context, English texts are included here for all the German pieces.

While singing in English, the following suggestions may be of use:

- Syllabic stress is most important. Lean on the accented syllables, and truly lighten unaccented syllables.
- Strive for a clear, supported tone. Keep vibrato to a minimum.
- Where there are double consonants (e.g., and die), articulate each one.
- When confronting diphthongs (e.g., house, way, rejoice, Christ), use the more rounded sound, and discard the second vowel.
- A beginning "r" may be flipped or trilled; an ending "r" may either be quickly flipped or not pronounced.
- All "s" sounds should be very short; an "l" should be sung with the tongue behind the front teeth.

While singing in Latin, it is helpful to use Germanic Latin pronunciation for Bach's music. A beginning "s" should be sung with a "z" sound, and soft "c" should be voiced as a "ts."

INSTRUMENTS

Most of Bach's choral works were intended to be sung with instruments in various combinations. The keyboard parts in this book are intended to be faithful to the original sources, but are still a substitute. Consider employing obbligato instruments—and feel free to use creative variety. Keyboard parts should be played in such a way that strong and weak beats are clearly articulated. In any case, directors should consult a full score in order to better understand the music and the arrangement.

HEARERS

Pitch level is often an issue in performance. At various places throughout Bach's life, pitch varied considerably, and many scholars agree that pitch in Leipzig at this time was A=415, a half step lower than present-day A=440. Some of the levels in this volume therefore are different than the original sources. Directors might wish to experiment with the pitch levels in order to determine what works best in a particular situation.

We hope that many will be blessed in the use of this book. As Johann Sebastian Bach, the Fifth Evangelist, frequently inscribed his work: To God alone the glory.

Richard Erickson and Mark Bighley

Savior of the Nations, Come

Nun komm, der Heiden Heiland

Soprano
Alto

1 Sav - ior of the na - tions, come;
2 Now your man - ger's ha - lo bright
3 Praise to God the Fa - ther sing,
Lob sei Gott dem Va - ter g'tan;

Tenor
Bass

3

vir - gin's son, make here your home. Dance in won - der,
hal - lows night with new - born light; let no night this
praise to God the Son, our king, praise to God the
Lob sei Gott seim ein' - gen Sohn, Lob sei Gott dem

6

all on earth: God has cho - sen such a birth.
light sub - due; let our faith shine ev - er new.
Spir - it be ev - er and e - ter - nal - ly.
Heil - gen Geist im - mer und in E - wig - keit.

Savior of the Nations, Come

Nun komm, der Heiden Heiland

10
of
the
na
-
tions,
come;
der
Hei
-
den
Hei
-
land,
10
13
16
Tenor
Sav
-
ior
of
the
na
-
tions,
Nun
komm,
der
Hei
-
den
Hei
-
16

19
come;
land,
Bass
Sav - ior
Nun komm,
19
22
of the na - tions, come;
der Hei - den Hei - land,
22

25
25
28
vir - gin's son, make here your
der Jung - frau - en Kind er -
vir - gin's son, make here your
der Jung - frau - en Kind er -
vir - gin's son, make here your
der Jung - frau - en Kind er -
vir - gin's son, make here your
der Jung - frau - en Kind er -
28

31
Gai
home.
kannt,
Dance in won - der,
daß sich wun - der
home.
kannt,
Dance in
daß sich
home.
kannt,
home.
kannt,
31
3
tr
II
8', 4'
35
all on earth, all on earth, all on
al - le Welt, al - le Welt, al - le
won - der, all on earth, all on
wun - der al - le Welt, al - le
Dance in won - der, all
daß sich wun - der al -
Dance in won - der,
daß sich wun - der
35

39

earth, dance in won - der, all on
Welt, daß sich wun - der al - le

earth, all on earth, dance in won - der, all on
Welt, al - le Welt, daß sich wun - der al - le

on earth, all on earth, all on
- le Welt, al - le Welt, al - le

all on earth, dance in won - der,
al - le Welt, daß sich wun - der

39

43

earth, dance in won - der, all on
Welt, daß sich wun - der al - le

earth, all on, all on earth, dance in
Welt, al - le, al - le Welt, daß sich

earth, dance in won - der, all on earth, dance in
Welt, daß sich wun - der al - le Welt, daß sich

all on earth, dance in won - der, all
al - le Welt, daß sich wun - der al -

43

47
earth, dance in won - der, all
Welt, daß sich wun - der al -
won - der, all on earth, all on, all
wun - der al - le Welt, al - le, al -
won - der, all on, all
wun - der al - le, al -
on earth, dance in won - der, all
- le Welt, daß sich wun - der al -
47
52
on earth, dance in won - der, all
- - le Welt, daß sich wun - der al -
on earth, dance in won - der, all
- - le Welt, daß sich wun - der al -
on earth, in won -
- - le Welt, sich wun -
- - -
52

57

— on, all on earth, all
- le, al - le Welt, al -

— on, all on earth, dance in won - der,
- le, al - le Welt, daß - sich wun - der

— der, all on earth, dance in won - der, all
- der al - le Welt, daß sich wun - der al -

— on earth,
- le Welt,

57

61

on —
- - le —

all on
al - le

— on — earth, all on earth, all on
- le — Welt, al - le Welt, al - le

dance in won - der, all on —
daß sich wun - der al - le —

61

65

earth, dance in won - der, all on
Welt, daß sich wun - der al - le

earth, dance in won - der, all
Welt, daß sich wun - der al -

earth, dance in won - der, all
Welt, daß sich wun - der al -

earth, dance in won - der,
Welt, daß sich wun - der

65

tr

69

earth, dance in won - der, all on
Welt, daß sich wun - der al - le

on earth, dance in won - der,
- le Welt, daß sich wun - der

on earth, dance in won - der,
- le Welt, daß sich wun - der

all on earth, dance in won - der,
al - le Welt, daß sich wun - der

69

73
earth, dance in won - der, all on earth, dance in
Welt, daß sich wun - der al - le Welt, daß sich
all on earth, dance in
al - le Welt, daß sich
all on earth, dance in won - der, all on
al - le Welt, daß sich wun - der al - le
all on earth, dance in won - der, all on
al - le Welt, daß sich wun - der al - le
73
77
won - der, all
wun - der al -
won - der, all
wun - der al -
earth, all on, all
Welt, al - le, al -
earth, dance in won - der, all
Welt, daß sich wun - der al -
77

81
on earth, dance in won - der, all on, all on
- le Welt, daß sich wun - der al - le, al - le
on earth, in won - der, all on
- le Welt, sich wun - der al - le
on earth, dance in won - der, all on
- le Welt, daß sich wun - der al - le
on
- - - le
81
tr
85
earth:
Welt,
earth:
Welt,
earth:
Welt,
earth:
Welt,
85
I

88
God has cho - sen such a
Gott solch Ge - burt ihm be -
God has cho - sen such a
Gott solch Ge - burt ihm be -
God has cho - sen such a
Gott solch Ge - burt ihm be -
God has cho - sen such a
Gott solch Ge - burt ihm be -
88
91
birth.
stellt.
birth.
stellt.
birth.
stellt.
birth.
stellt.
91

Wake, Awake, for Night is Flying

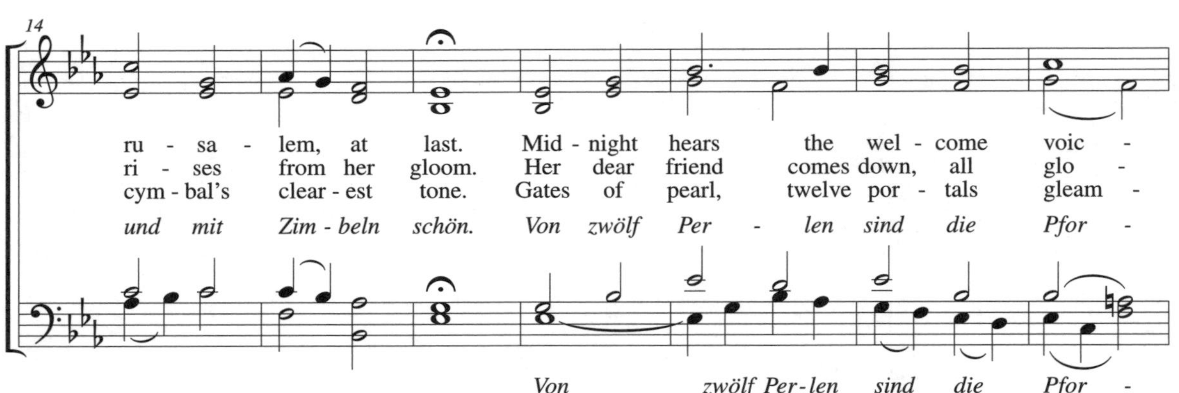

28
"Come forth, you maid-ens! Night is past. The bride - groom
her star is ris'n; her light is come. Now come, O
with an - gel choirs a - round your throne. No eye has
der En - gel hoch um dei - nen Thron. Kein Aug hat
35
comes! A - wake; your lamps with glad - ness take!"
Bless - ed One, Lord Je - sus, God's own Son.
caught the light, no ear the thun - 'd'ring might
je ges - pürt, kein Ohr hat je ge - hört
41
Al - le - lu - ia! A - rise, pre - pare, the
Sing ho - san - na! Oh, hear the call! Come
of such glo - ry. There we will go: what
sol - che Freu - de. Das sind wir froh, i -
47
feast is here; go, meet the Lord as he draws near.
one, come all, and fol - low to the ban - quet hall.
joy we'll know! There sweet de - light will ev - er flow.
o, i - o, e - wig in dul - ci ju - bi - lo.

Zion Hears the Watchmen Singing

Zion hört die Wächter singen

16
and all her heart_ with joy is spring -
das Herz tut ihr___ vor Freu - de sprin -
19
ing. She wakes, she ri - ses___ from her
gen, sie wacht und ste - het___ ei - lend
22
gloom.
auf.
25

28
31
tr
tr
tr
34
Her dear friend comes down, all glo - rious,
Ihr Freund kommt vom Him - mel präch - tig,
37
the strong in grace,_ in truth vic - tor -
von Gna - den stark,_ von Wahr - heit mäch -

40
ious: her star is ris'n; her___ light is
tig, ihr Licht wird hell, ihr___ Stern geht
43
come.
auf.
46
tr
49
tr
tr
tr
Now come, O Bless - ed
Nun komm, du wer - te

52
One,
Kron,
Lord Je - sus, God's own Son.
Herr Je - su, Got - tes Sohn!
55
Sing ho - san - na!
Ho - si - an - na!
58
61
tr

63
Oh, hear the call!
Wir fol - gen all
Come
zum
66
one, come all,
Freu - den - saal
and fol - low
und hal - ten
69
to the ban - quet hall.
mit das A - bend - mahl.
tr
72
tr

Gloria in excelsis Deo

*Optional C instrument part is on p. 154.

glo - ri - a, glo - ri - a in ex - cel - sis De - o!
glo - ri - a, glo - ri - a in ex - cel - sis De - o!
glo - ri - a, glo - ri - a in ex - cel - sis De - o!
glo - ri - a in ex - cel - sis De - o!
Et in ter - ra pax, et in ter - ra pax, in ter - ra
Et in ter - ra pax, in ter - ra pax, in ter - ra
Et in ter - ra pax, in ter - ra pax, in ter - ra
Et in ter - ra pax, in ter - ra
II

10
bo - na vo-
pax ho - mi - ni - bus, bo-na, bo - na vo - lun-tas, bo-na, bo - na vo -
pax ho - mi - ni - bus, bo-na, bo - na vo - lun-tas, bo-na, bo - na vo-
pax ho - mi - ni - bus, bo-na, bo - na vo-lun-tas, bo-na, bo - na vo -
pax ho - mi - ni-bus, bo-na, bo - na vo-lun-tas, bo-na, bo - na vo -
10
(II)
I
lun-tas, bo-na, bo - na vo - lun - tas,
13
lun-tas, bo-na, bo - na vo - lun-tas, bo-na, bo - na vo - lun-tas, bo-na, bo - na vo-
lun-tas, bo-na vo - lun - tas, bo-na vo - lun-tas, bo-na, bo - na vo -
lun-tas, bo-na vo - lun - tas, bo-na vo - lun-tas, bo-na, bo - na vo-
lun-tas, bo-na, bo - na vo-lun-tas, bo-na, bo - na vo-lun-tas, bo-na, bo - na vo -
13

16

lun - tas, bo - na, bo - na vo - lun - tas, bo - na vo -

lun - tas, bo - na, bo - na vo - lun - tas, bo - na, bo - na vo -

lun - tas, bo - na, bo - na vo - lun - tas, bo - na, bo - na vo -

lun - tas, bo - na, bo - na vo - lun - tas, bo - na, bo - na vo-

16

18

bo - na vo - lun - tas, bo - na vo - lun - tas.

lun - tas, bo - na vo - lun - tas, bo - na, bo - na vo - lun - tas.

lun - tas, bo - na, bo - na vo - lun - tas.

lun - tas,_ bo - na, bo - na vo - lun - tas, vo - lun - tas, vo - lun - tas.

lun-tas, bo - na, bo - na vo - lun - tas, bo - na, bo - na___ vo - lun - tas.

18

From Heaven Above to Earth I Come

Vom Himmel hoch, da komm ich her

5
earth I come
komm ich her,
come, from heav'n a - bove to earth I come to bring good
her, vom Him - mel hoch, da komm ich her, ich bring euch
from heav'n a - bove to earth I come to bring good news to
vom Him - mel hoch, da komm ich her, ich bring euch gu - te
come, to earth I come
her, da komm ich her,
5
II
7
to
ich
news to ev - 'ry - one, to bring good news to
gu - te neu - e Mär, ich bring euch gu - te
ev - 'ry - one, to bring good news to ev -
neu - e Mär, ich bring euch gu - te neu -
to bring good news to ev - 'ry - one, to bring good
ich bring euch gu - te neu - e Mär, ich bring euch
7
(II)
I

9
bring good news to
bring euch gu - te
ev - 'ry - one, good news to ev - 'ry -
neu - e Mär, euch gu - te neu - e
- 'ry - one, to bring good news to ev - 'ry -
- e Mär, ich bring euch gu - te neu - e
news to ev - 'ry - one, to bring good
gu - te neu - e Mär, ich bring euch
9
11
ev - 'ry - one!
neu - e Mär,
one, to bring good news to ev - 'ry - one! Glad ti - dings
Mär, ich bring euch gu - te neu - e Mär, der gu - ten
one, to bring good news to ev - 'ry - one!
Mär, ich bring euch gu - te neu - e Mär,
news, good news to ev - 'ry - one!
gu - te neu - e, neu - e Mär,
11
II

13
of great joy I bring, great joy, glad ti - dings of great joy I
Mär bring ich so viel, so viel, der gu - ten Mär bring ich so
Glad ti - dings of great joy I bring, glad ti - dings of great
der gu - ten Mär bring ich so viel, so viel, bring ich so
Glad ti - dings of great joy I
der gu - ten Mär bring ich so
13
(II)
I
15
Glad ti - dings
der gu - ten
bring, I bring great joy, great joy, glad ti - dings of great joy I
viel, bring ich so viel, so viel, der gu - ten Mär bring ich so
joy, glad ti - dings of great joy, glad ti - dings
viel, bring ich so viel, so viel, der gu - ten
bring, glad ti - dings of great joy I bring, great joy I bring, great
viel, der gu - ten Mär bring ich so viel, so viel, bring ich so
15

17
of great joy I
Mär bring ich so
bring, great joy I bring, great joy, great joy I bring,
viel, bring ich so viel, so viel, so viel, bring ich
of great joy I bring, great joy, great joy I bring, great
Mär bring ich so viel, so viel, bring ich so viel, so
joy, glad ti - dings of great joy I bring, glad ti - dings of great joy I
viel, der gu - ten Mär bring ich so viel, der gu - ten Mär bring ich so
17
19
bring
viel,
great joy I bring, great joy to all the world, and
so viel, bring ich so viel, da - von ich singn und
joy I bring, great joy to all the world,
viel, bring ich so viel, da - von ich singn
bring, glad ti - dings of great joy, great joy
viel, der gu - ten Mär bring ich so viel,
19
II

21
to
da -
glad - ly sing, and glad - ly sing,
sa - gen will, ich singn und sa - gen will,
and glad - ly sing, and glad - ly
und sa - gen will, da - von ich
to all the world, and glad - ly sing, and glad - ly
da - von ich singn und sa - gen will, und sa - gen
21
(II)
I
23
all the world, and
von ich singn und
to all the world, and glad - ly
da - von ich singn und sa - gen
sing, and glad - ly sing, to all the world, and
singn und sa - gen will, da - von ich singn und
sing, to all the world, and glad - ly
will, da - von ich singn und sa - gen
23

25

glad - ly
sa - gen

sing, and glad - ly__ sing, to all the world, and glad - ly
will, da - von________ ich__ singn, da - von ich singn und sa - gen

glad - ly__ sing, to all the world, and glad - ly
sa - gen__ will, da - von ich singn und sa - gen

sing, to all the world, and glad - ly
will, da - von ich singn und sa - gen

25

27

sing.
will.

sing, to all the world, and glad - ly__ sing.
will, da - von ich singn und sa - gen__ will.

sing, to all the world, and__ glad - ly__ sing.
will, da-von ich singn und__ sa - gen__ will.

sing, to all the world, and glad - ly__ sing.
will, da-von ich singn und sa - gen__ will.

27

From Heaven Above to Earth I Come

Ach mein herzliebes Jesulein

O Morning Star, How Fair and Bright!

Wie bin ich doch so herzlich froh

10
you have won our hearts to serve you on - ly!
and a - bove: this is your great sal - va - tion.
hap - py place be - yond all tears and sin - ning!
Pa - ra - deis; des klopf ich in die Hän - de.
13
Low - ly, ho - ly! Great and glor - ious, all vic - to - rious,
Al - le - lu - ia! Christ the liv - ing, to us giv - ing
A - men! A - men! Come, Lord Je - sus! Crown of glad - ness!
A - men, a - men, komm du schö - ne Freu - den - kro - ne,
17
rich in bless - ing! Rule and might o'er all pos - sess - ing!
life for - ev - er, keeps us yours and fails us nev - er!
We are yearn - ing for the day of your re - turn - ing.
bleib night lan - ge; dei - ner wart ich mit Ver - lan - gen.

Break Forth, O Beauteous Heavenly Light

Brich an, o schönes Morgenlicht

Bring Low Our Ancient Adam

Ertöt uns durch dein Güte

7
then
er -
fore -
Va -
9
raise us by your grace.
weck uns durch dein Gnad.
told by an - cient seers,
ters in E - wig - keit,
11

13
Lift up to life e -
Den al - ten Men - schen
by God the Fa - ther
aus seim Her - zen ent -

15
ter - nal
krän - ke,
giv - en,
spros - sen,

17
our
fal - len
hu - man
daß
der
neu'
le - ben
in
hu - man
form
ap -
gleich - wie
ge - schrie - ben
19
race—
mag
pears.
steht,
21
to
und
No
er

23
life that finds its mea - sure,
hier auf die - ser Er - den,
sphere his light con - fin - ing,
ist der Mor - gen - ster - ne,
25
its
den
no
sein
27
clar - i - ty and plea - sure,
Sinn und alls Be - geh - ren
star so bright - ly shin - ing
Glän - zen streckt er fer - ne

29
in
und
as
vor
31
you, Cre - a - tor God.
G'dan - ken hab zu dir.
he, our Morn - ing Star.
an - dern Ster - nen klar.
33

Chorale
Soprano
Alto
Tenor
Bass
Cre - a - tor God, who made us: all things are in your pow'r.
Du Schöp-fer al - le Din - ge, du vä - ter - li - che Kraft,
Alternate text: A - wak - en, Lord, our spir - it to know and love you more,
Laß uns in dei - ner Lie - be und Kennt - nis neh - men zu,
5
You gov - ern start to fin - ish our ev - 'ry mor - tal hour.
re - gierst von End zu En - de kräf - tig aus eig - ner Macht.
in faith to stand un - shak - en, in spir - it to a - dore,
daß wir am Glau - ben blei - ben, dir die - nen im Geist so,
9
Draw in our hearts, en - fold them— at - tract our
Das Herz uns zu dir wen - de und kehr ab
that we, through this world mov - ing, each glimpse of
daß wir hier mö - gen schmek - ken dein Sü - ßig -
12
sens - es, hold them— su - preme, tran - scen - dent force.
un - sre Sin - ne, daß sie nicht irrn von dir.
heav - en prov - ing, may reap its full - ness there.
keit im Her - zen und dür - sten stets nach dir.

Transcendent, Holy God

Dem wir das Heilig itzt

9
mu - sic vast re - sound - ing,
Freu - den las - sen klin - gen
II
I
I
12
let us ac - knowl - edge you, our
und mit der En - gel - schar das
II
I
15
thanks and praise com - pound - ing—
Hei - lig, Hei - lig sin - gen,
I
II
I

18
un - til__ with all__ the__ saints, ec -
den herz - lich_ lobt_ und_ preist die__
II
I
II

21
stat - ic__ at__ your throne,
gan - ze__ Chri - sten - heit:
I

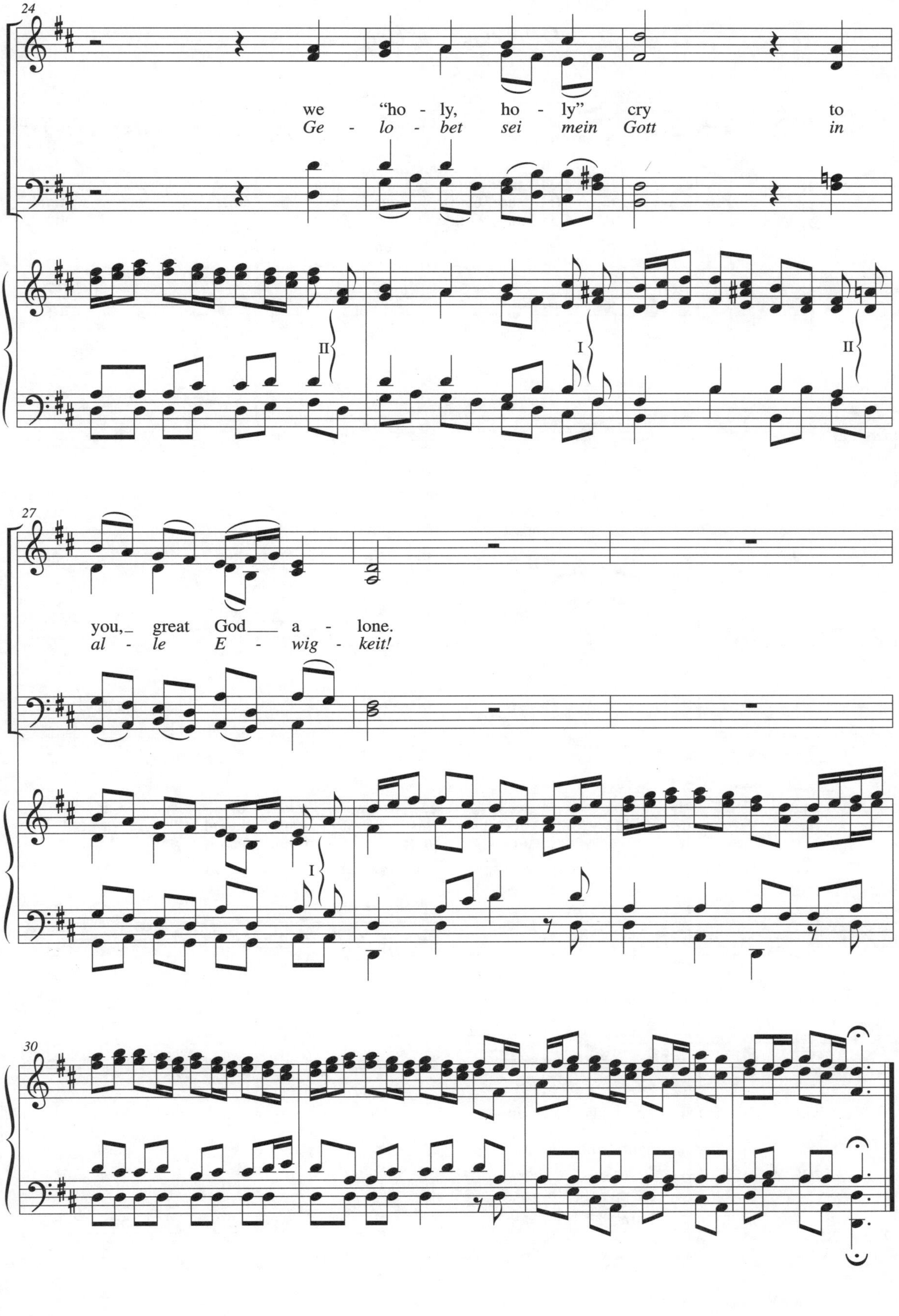

we "ho - ly, ho - ly" cry to
Ge - lo - bet sei mein Gott in

you, great God a - lone.
al - le E - wig - keit!

II

I

II

I

All Creatures Great and Small

Gelobet sei der Herr

Jesus, My Sweet Pleasure

Jesu, meine Freude

8
fret - ted, my de - sire so whet - ted, long - ing af - ter
lan - ge ist dem Her - zen ban - ge und_ ver - langt nach
fret - ted, my_ de - sire so whet - ted, long - ing af - ter
lan - ge ist_ dem Her - zen ban - ge und_ ver - langt nach
fret - ted, my_ de - sire so_ whet - ted, long - ing af - ter
lan - ge ist_ dem_ Her - zen_ ban - ge und ver - langt nach
fret - ted, my de - sire so_ whet - ted, long - ing_ af - ter
lan - ge ist dem_ Her - zen_ ban - ge und ver - langt nach
8
12
you! Lamb of God, my own be-trothed, noth - ing in this
dir! Got - tes Lamm, mein Bräu - ti - gam, au - ßer dir soll
you! Lamb of God, my own be - trothed, noth - ing in this_
dir! Got - tes Lamm, mein Bräu - ti - gam, au - ßer dir soll_
you! Lamb of God, my own be - trothed, noth - ing in this
dir! Got - tes Lamm, mein Bräu - ti - gam, au - ßer dir soll
you! Lamb of God, my own be - trothed, noth - ing in this_
dir! Got - tes Lamm, mein Bräu - ti - gam, au - ßer_ dir soll_
12

16
life so moves me, holds me gently, soothes me.
mir auf Er - den nichts sonst Lie - bers wer - den.
life so moves me, holds me gen - tly, soothes me.
mir auf Er - den nichts sonst Lie - bers wer - den.
life so moves me, holds me gen - tly, soothes me.
mir auf Er - den nichts sonst Lie - bers wer - den.
life so moves me, holds me gen - tly, soothes me.
mir auf Er - den nichts sonst Lie - bers wer - den.
16
20
divisi
2 You pro - vide my re - fuge from the driv - ing
2 Un - ter dei - nem Schir - men bin ich vor den
2 You pro - vide my re - fuge from the driv - ing
2 Un - ter dei - nem Schir - men bin ich vor den
2 You pro - vide my re - fuge from the driv - ing
2 Un - ter dei - nem Schir - men bin ich vor den
2 You pro - vide my re - fuge from the driv - ing
2 Un - ter dei - nem Schir - men bin ich vor den
20

23
del - uge of__ the dev - il's band. Let the tempt - er
Stür - men al - ler Fein - de frei. Laß den Sa - tan
del - uge of__ the__ dev - il's band. Let the tempt - er__
Stür - men al - ler__ Fein - de frei. Laß den Sa - tan__
del - uge of__ the__ dev - il's band. Let__ the__ tempt - er__
Stür - men al - ler__ Fein - de frei. Laß den__ Sa - tan__
del - uge of__ the__ dev - il's band. Let__ the tempt-er
Stür - men al - ler__ Fein - de frei. Laß__ den Sa - tan
23
27
trail__ me, en - e - mies as - sail__ me, Je - sus is at
wit - tern, laß die Welt er - bit - tern, mir__ steht Je - sus
trail__ me, en - e - mies as - sail__ me, Je - sus__ is__ at
wit - tern, laß__ die Welt er - bit - tern, mir__ steht Je - sus
trail__ me, en - e - mies as - sail__ me, Je - sus__ is at
wit - tern, laß die Welt er - bit - tern, mir__ steht Je - sus
trail__ me, en - e - mies as - sail me, Je - sus__ is at
wit - tern, laß__ die Welt er - bit - tern, mir__ steht Je - sus
27

When the rain of fear and pain,
Ob es itzt gleich kracht und blitzt,

31

hand! When the rain of fear, of fear and pain, when the storms of
bei. Ob es itzt gleich kracht, gleich kracht und blitzt, ob_ gleich Sünd und

hand! When the rain of fear and pain, fear and pain, when the storms of__
bei. Ob es itzt gleich kracht und blitzt, kracht und blitzt, ob gleich Sünd und__

hand! When the rain of fear and pain, fear and pain, when the storms of
bei. Ob__ es itzt gleich kracht und blitzt, kracht und blitzt, ob gleich Sünd und

hand! When______ the rain of fear and pain, when______ the storms of
bei. Ob______ es itzt gleich kracht und blitzt, ob______ gleich Sünd und

31

35

hell be - set___ me, Je - sus will pro - tect___ me.
Höl - le__ schrek - ken: Je - sus will mich__ dek - ken.

hell__ be - set___ me, Je - sus__ will pro - tect___ me.
Höl - le__ schrek - ken: Je - sus__ will mich__ dek - ken.

hell__ be - set______ me, Je - sus will pro - tect______ me.
Höl - le__ schrek - ken: Je - sus will mich__ dek - ken.

hell__ be - set_____ me, Je - sus will pro - tect____ me.
Höl - le__ schrek - ken: Je - sus will mich dek - ken.

35

39
3 Gone with bra - zen trea - sure!
3 Weg mit al - len Schät - zen;
3 Gone, gone with bra - zen trea - sure, with bra - zen
3 Weg, weg mit al - len Schät - zen, mit al - len
3 Gone, gone, be - gone with bra - zen trea - sure, with bra - zen
3 Weg, weg, weg, weg mit al - len Schät - zen, mit al - len
3 Gone, gone, be - gone, with bra - zen trea - sure!
3 Weg, weg, weg, weg mit al - len Schät - zen;
39
41
You are all my plea - sure,
du bist mein Er - göt - zen,
trea - sure! You, you are all my plea - sure, Je -
Schät - zen; du, du bist mein Er - göt - zen, Je -
trea - sure! You, you are all my plea - sure,
Schät - zen; du, du bist mein Er - göt - zen,
You, you are all my plea - sure, Je - sus,
du, du bist mein Er - göt - zen, Je - su,
41

43
Je - sus, all my own.
Je - su, mei - ne Lust.
- sus, all my own, all my own.
- su, mei - ne Lust, mei - ne Lust.
Je - sus, all my own.
Je - su, mei - ne Lust.
Je - sus, all my own, all my own.
Je - su, mei - ne Lust, mei - ne Lust.
43
45
Gone, fare - well to glo - ry!
Weg, ihr eit - len Eh - ren,
Gone, gone, fare - well to glo - ry, fare - well to
Weg, weg, ihr eit - len Eh - ren, ihr eit - len
Gone, gone, be - gone, fare - well to glo - ry, fare - well to
Weg, weg, weg, weg, ihr eit - len Eh - ren, ihr eit - len
Gone, gone, be - gone, fare - well to glo - ry!
Weg, weg, weg, weg, ihr eit - len Eh - ren,
45

47
I shall not be sor - ry
ich mag euch nicht hö - ren,
glo - ry! I, I shall not be sor - ry to
Eh - ren, ich, ich mag euch nicht hö - ren, bleibt
8
glo - ry! I, I shall not be sor - ry
Eh - ren, ich, ich mag euch nicht hö - ren,
I, I shall not be sor - ry, to re -
ich, ich mag euch nicht hö - ren, bleibt mir,
47
49
to re - main un - known.
bleibt mir un - be - wußt!
re - main un - known, re - main un - known.
mir un - be - wusst, un - be - wußt!
8
to re - main un - known.
bleibt mir un - be - wußt!
main, re - main un - known, re - main un - known.
bleibt mir un - be - wußt, un - be - wußt!
49

51
Troub - les, pain, cross, death, or shame,
E - lend, Not, Kreuz, Schmach, und Tod
Troub - les, pain, cross, death, or shame, death or
E - lend, Not, Kreuz, Schmach, und Tod, Schmach und
Troub - les, pain, cross, death, or shame, death or
E - lend, Not, Kreuz, Schmach, und Tod, Schmach und
Troub - les, pain, cross, death, or shame,
E - lend, Not, Kreuz, Schmach, und Tod
51
53
from his side they can - not force
soll mich, ob ich viel muß lei -
shame, from his side they can - not force
Tod soll mich, ob ich viel muß lei -
shame, from his side they can - not force
Tod soll mich, ob ich viel muß lei -
from his side they can - not force
soll mich, ob ich viel muß lei -
53

55
me nor from him di - vorce me.
den, nicht von Je - sus schei - den.
me, nor, nor from him di - vorce me.
den, nicht, nicht von Je - sus schei - den.
me, nor, nor from him di - vorce me, from him di - vorce me.
den, nicht, nicht von Je - sus schei - den, von Je - sus schei - den.
me, nor, nor, nor, nor from him di - vorce me.
den, nicht, nicht, nicht, nicht von Je - sus schei - den.
55
58
4 Qui - et, fears and sad - ness, for the Lord of
4 Weicht, ihr Trau - er - geis - ter, denn mein Freu - den -
4 Qui - et, fears and sad - ness, for the Lord of
4 Weicht, ihr Trau - er - geis - ter, denn mein Freu - den -
4 Qui - et, fears and sad - ness, for the Lord of
4 Weicht, ihr Trau - er - geis - ter, denn mein Freu - den -
4 Qui - et, fears and sad - ness, for the Lord of
4 Weicht, ihr Trau - er - geis - ter, denn mein Freu - den -
58

61
glad - ness, Je - sus, en - ters in. Sick - ness, death, and
meis - ter, Je - sus, tritt her - ein. De - nen, die Gott
glad - ness, Je - sus, en - ters in. Sick - ness, death, and
meis - ter, Je - sus, tritt her - ein. De - nen, die_ Gott
glad - ness, Je - sus, en - ters in. Sick - ness, death, and
meis - ter, Je - sus, tritt her - ein. De - nen, die_ Gott
glad - ness, Je - sus,_ en - ters in. Sick - ness, death, and
meis - ter, Je - sus,_ tritt her - ein. De - nen, die Gott
61
65
mourn - ing, love of God trans - form - ing, gives sweet peace with-
lie - ben, muß auch ihr Be - trü - ben lau - ter Zuk - ker
mourn - ing, love of God trans - form - ing, gives sweet peace with-
lie - ben, muß auch ihr Be - trü - ben lau - ter Zuk - ker
mourn - ing, love of__ God trans - form - ing, gives sweet peace with -
lie - ben, muß auch ihr Be - trü - ben lau - ter Zuk - ker
mourn - ing, love of__ God trans - form - ing, gives sweet peace with -
lie - ben, muß auch ihr Be - trü - ben lau - ter__ Zuk - ker
65

69

in. I have borne this world - ly scorn, yet in grief I
sein. Duld ich schon hier Spott und Hohn, den - noch bleibst du

in. I have borne this world - ly scorn, yet in grief I
sein. Duld ich schon hier Spott und Hohn, den - noch bleibst du

in. I have borne this world - ly scorn, yet in grief I
sein. Duld ich schon hier Spott und Hohn, den - noch bleibst du

in. I have borne this world - ly scorn, yet in grief I
sein. Duld ich schon hier Spott und Hohn, den - noch bleibst du

69

73

find my trea - sure, Je - sus, per - fect plea - sure.
auch im Lei - de, Je - su, mei - ne Freu - de.

find my trea - sure, Je - sus, per - fect plea - sure.
auch im Lei - de, Je - su, mei - ne Freu - de.

find my trea - sure, Je - sus, per - fect plea - sure.
auch im Lei - de, Je - su, mei - ne Freu - de.

find my trea - sure, Je - sus, per - fect plea - sure.
auch im Lei - de, Je - su, mei - ne Freu - de.

73

O Sacred Head, Now Wounded

O Haupt voll Blut und Wunden

Crucifixus

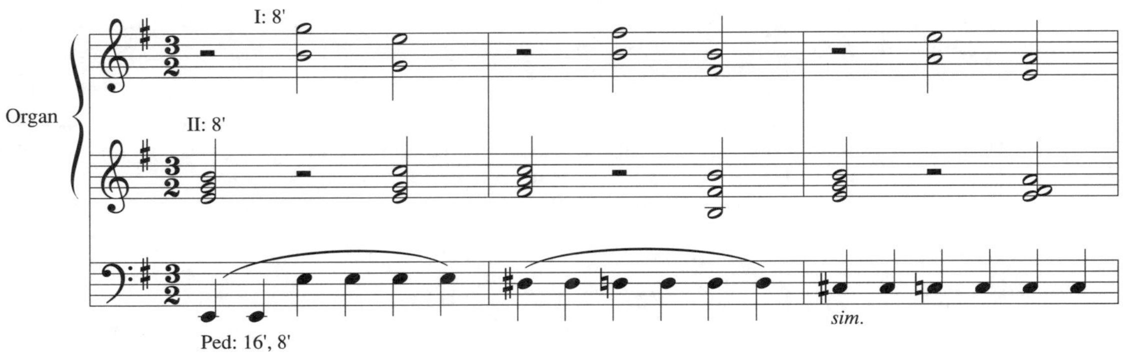

4

Soprano

Cru - ci - fi - xus,

Alto

Cru - ci - fi - xus,

Tenor

Cru - ci -

Bass

4

Translation: He was crucified for our sake under Pontius Pilate; he suffered death and was buried.

8
cru - ci - fi - xus,
fi - xus,
cru - ci - fi - xus
Cru - ci - fi - xus,
cru - ci -
8
12
cru - ci - fi - xus e - ti - am pro
cru - ci - fi - xus
cru - ci - fi - xus
fi - xus,
cru - ci -
12

16
no - bis,
cru - ci -
e - ti - am pro no - bis,
cru - ci - fi - xus e - ti - am, pro
fi - xus,
cru - ci - fi - xus e -
16
20
fi - xus
e - ti - am pro
e - ti - am pro no - bis sub
no - bis,
e -
- ti - am pro no - bis,
20

24
no - bis sub Pon - ti - o Pi -
Pon - ti - o Pi - la - to, sub Pon - ti -
- ti - am pro no - - bis sub Pon - ti - o Pi -
sub Pon - ti - o Pi -
24
28
- la - to, pas - sus et se - pul -
o Pi - la - to, pas - sus et se -
la - to, pas - sus, pas - sus et se -
la - to, pas - sus et se -
28

32

- tus est, pas - sus et se - pul - tus

pul - tus est, pas - sus_ et se - pul - tus_

pul - tus est, pas - sus_ et se - pul - tus

pul - tus est, pas - sus et se - pul - tus

32

36

est, cru - ci - fi - xus e - ti -

est, cru - ci -

est, cru -

est,

36

40
am pro no - bis sub Pon - ti - o Pi -
fi - - xus e - ti - am pro no - bis sub
- ci - fi - xus
cru - ci - fi - xus
40
43
la - - to, pas -
Pon - ti - o Pi - la - to, pas - sus et se -
e - ti - am pro no - bis pas - sus
e - ti - am pro no - bis
43

47

- sus et se - pul - tus est, se -

pul - tus, se - pul - tus est, pas -

et se - pul - tus est, se -

pas - sus et se - pul - tus est, se -

47

50

pul - tus est, se - pul - tus est.

- sus et se - pul - tus est.

pul - tus, se - pul - tus est.

pul - tus est, et se - pul - tus est.

50

Christ Is Arisen

Christ ist erstanden

6
full and free, for Christ our com - fort true will be.
froh sein; Chri - stus will un - ser Trost sein.
full and free, for Christ our com - fort true will be.
froh sein; Chri - stus will un - ser Trost sein.
full and free, for Christ our com - fort true will be.
froh sein; Chri - stus will un - ser Trost sein.
full and free, for Christ our com - fort true will be.
froh sein; Chri - stus will un - ser Trost sein.
6
9
Ky - ri - e - leis. Were Christ not a -
Ky - ri - e - leis. Wär er nicht er -
Ky - ri - e - leis. Were Christ not a -
Ky - ri - e - leis. Wär er nicht er -
Ky - ri - e - leis. Were Christ not a -
Ky - ri - e - leis. Wär er nicht er -
Ky - ri - e - leis. Were Christ not a -
Ky - ri - e - leis. Wär er nicht er -
9

12
ris - en, then death_ were_ still_ our pris - on. He
stan - den, so wär__ die__ Welt_ ver - gan - gen; seit
ris - en, then death were_ still_ our pris - on. He
stan - den, so wär die__ Welt_ ver - gan - gen; seit
ris - en, then_ death were still_ our pris - on. He
stan - den, so___ wär_ die Welt_ ver - gan - gen; seit
ris - en, then death were still_ our__ pris - on. He
stan - den, so wär die Welt_ ver - gan - gen; seit
12
15
lives in - deed! We are re - stored; sing praise to___ Je - sus
daß er nun er - stan - den ist, so lo - ben__wir den
lives_ in - deed!_ We_ are re - stored; sing_ praise to Je - sus
daß__ er nun__ er - stan - den ist, so__ lo - ben wir den
lives_ in - deed!__ We are re - stored; sing_ praise to__ Je - sus
daß__ er nun___ er - stan - den ist, so___ lo - ben_ wir__ den
lives_ in - deed! We are_ re - stored; sing_ praise________ to Je - sus
daß_ er___ nun er - stan - den_ ist, so__ lo - ben wir den
15

18
Christ, our Lord. Ky - ri - e - leis.
Her - ren Christ. Ky - ri - e - leis.
Christ, our Lord. Ky - ri - e - leis.
Her - ren Christ. Ky - ri - e - leis.
Christ, our Lord. Ky - ri - e - leis.
Her - ren Christ. Ky - ri - e - leis.
Christ, our Lord. Ky - ri - e - leis.
Her - ren Christ. Ky - ri - e - leis.
18
21
Hal - le - lu - jah, hal - le - lu - jah, hal - le - lu - jah! So
Hal - le - lu - ja, hal - le - lu - ja, hal - le - lu - ja! Des
Hal - le - lu - jah, hal - le - lu - jah, hal - le - lu - jah! So
Hal - le - lu - ja, hal - le - lu - ja, hal - le - lu - ja! Des
Hal - le - lu - jah, hal - le - lu - jah, hal - le - lu - jah! So
Hal - le - lu - ja, hal - le - lu - ja, hal - le - lu - ja! Des
Hal - le - lu - jah, hal - le - lu - jah, hal - le - lu - jah! So
Hal - le - lu - ja, hal - le - lu - ja, hal - le - lu - ja! Des
21

25
let our joy rise full and free, for Christ our com - fort
solln wir al - le froh sein; Chri - stus will un - ser
let our joy rise full and free, for Christ our com - fort
solln wir al - le froh sein; Chri - stus will un - ser
let our joy rise full and free, for Christ our com - fort
solln wir al - le froh sein; Chri - stus will un - ser
let our joy rise full and free, for Christ our com - fort
solln wir al - le froh sein; Chri - stus will un - ser
25
28
true will be. Ky - ri - e - leis.
Trost sein. Ky - ri - e - leis.
true will be. Ky - ri - e - leis.
Trost sein. Ky - ri - e - leis.
true will be. Ky - ri - e - leis.
Trost sein. Ky - ri - e - leis.
true will be. Ky - ri - e - leis.
Trost sein. Ky - ri - e - leis.
28

Lord Jesus Christ, God's Only Son

Jesus Christus, Gottes Sohn

9
in our stead de - scend - ed:
un - ser Statt ist kom - men
11
13
the
und
15
knot of sin has been un - done,
hat die Sün - de ab - ge - tan,

17
the claim of
da - mit dem
19
death is end - ed.
Tod ge - nom - men
21
23
Christ has crushed the___ pow'r of hell;
all sein Recht und___ sein Ge - walt;

25
Adagio
now there is naught but
da blei - bet nichts denn
27
Allegro
death's gray shell—
Tods Ge - stalt,
29
its
den
31
sting is lost for - ev - er.
Stach'l hat er ver - lo - ren.

33
Hal - le - lu - jah, hal - le - lu -
Hal - le - lu - ja, hal - le - lu -
35
jah, hal - le - lu - jah,
hal - le - lu-
ja, hal - le - lu - ja,
hal - le - lu-
37
jah, hal,
hal - le - lu-jah!
ja, hal,
hal - le - lu-ja!
39
41

Christ Jesus Lay in Death's Strong Bands

Wir essen und leben wohl

*or holy day

Come, Holy Ghost, God and Lord

Du heilige Brunst, süßer Trost

14
ho - ly faith your Church u - nite; from ev - 'ry land
none but Christ our mas - ter be, that we in liv -
to our weak - ness strength im - part, that brave - ly here
stärk des Flei - sches Blö - dig - keit, daß wir hier rit - ter -

this to your praise, O Lord, our God,
in him, our Lord, with all our might
through life and death to you, our Lord,
durch Tod und Le - ben zu dir

17
and ev - 'ry tongue, this to your praise, O Lord, our God, be
- ing faith a - bide, in him, our Lord, with all our might con -
we may con - tend, through life and death to you, our Lord, as -
- lich rin - gen, durch Tod und Le - ben zu dir drin-

this to your praise, O Lord, our God,
in him, our Lord, with all our might
through life and death to you, our Lord,
durch Tod und Le - ben zu dir drin -

be sung:
con - fide. Al - le - lu - ia, al - le - lu - ia!
as - cend.
drin - gen. Hal - le - lu - ja, hal - le - lu - ja!

21
sung:
- fide. Al - le - lu - ia, al - le - lu - ia!
- cend.
- gen. Hal - le - lu - ja, hal - le - lu - ja!

be sung:
con - fide. Al - le - lu - ia, al - le - lu - ia!
as - cend.
- gen. Hal - le - lu - ja, hal - le - lu - ja!

Lord, Keep Us Steadfast in Your Word

Erhalt uns, Herr, bei deinem Wort

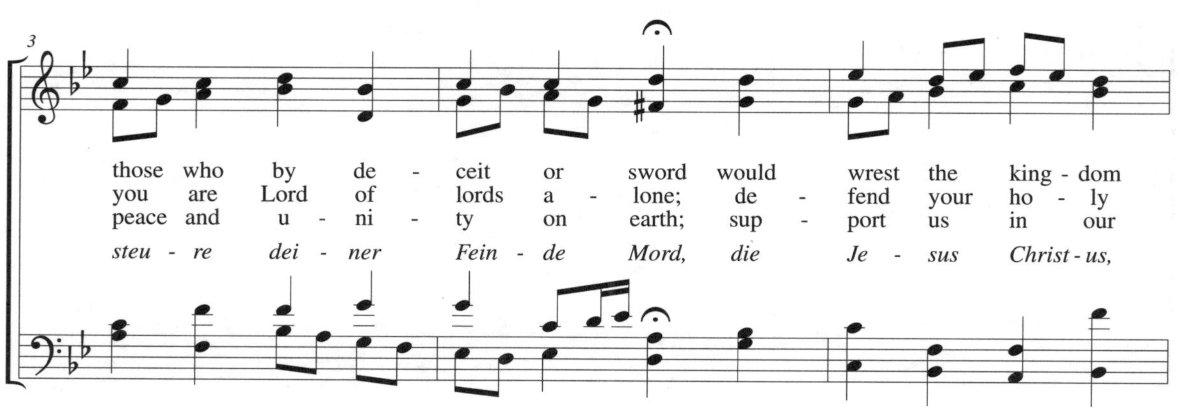

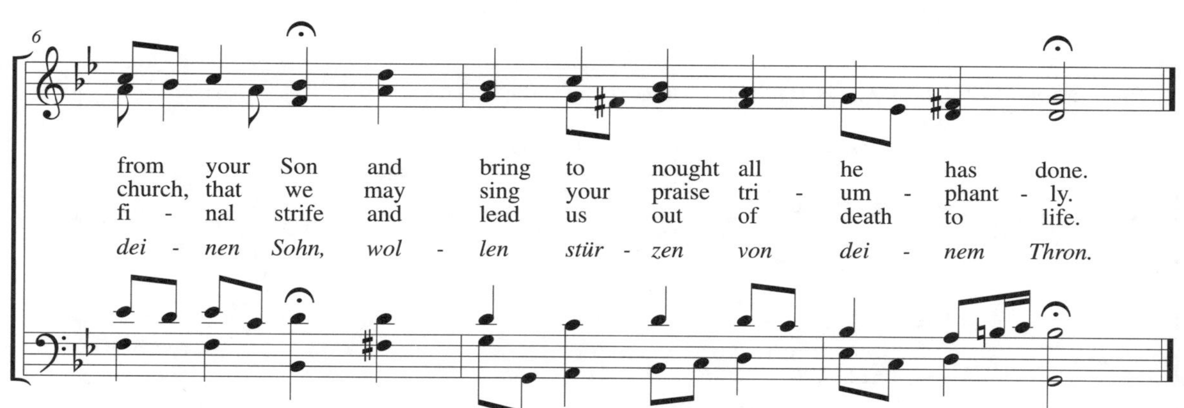

A Mighty Fortress Is Our God

Ein feste Burg ist unser Gott

Lord, Thee I Love with All My Heart

Ach Herr, laß dein lieb Engelein

And should my heart for sor - row break, my trust in thee can
Let no false doc - trine me be - guile, let Sa - tan not my
And then from death a - wak - en me, that these my eyes with
Als - dann vom Tod er - wek - ke mich, daß mei - ne Au - gen
noth - ing shake. Thou art the por - tion I have sought; thy pre - cious blood my
soul de - file. Give strength and pa - tience un - to me to bear my cross and
joy may see, O Son of God, thy glo - rious face, my Sav - ior and my
se - hen dich in al - ler Freud, o Got - tes Sohn, mein Hei - land und Ge -
soul has bought. Lord Je - sus Christ, my God and Lord, my
fol - low thee. Lord Je - sus Christ, my God and Lord, my
fount of grace. Lord Je - sus Christ, my prayer at - tend, my
na - den - thron. Herr Je - su Christ, er - hö - re mich, er -
God and Lord, for - sake me not! I trust thy Word.
God and Lord, in death thy com - fort still af - ford.
prayer at - tend, and I will praise thee with - out end!
hö - re mich. Ich will dich prei - sen e - wig - lich.

O Jesus Christ, My Life, My Light

O Jesu Christ, meins Lebens Licht

16
Soprano
1 O
2 Your
Alto
1 O Je - sus
2 Your death and
Tenor
1 O
2 Your
Bass
16
Fine
II
20
Je - sus Christ, my
death and life will
Christ, my life, my light,
life will be my stay,
Je - sus Christ, my life, my light, O
death and life will be my stay, your
1 O Je - sus
2 Your death and
20

24
life, my light,
be my stay
O Je - sus Christ, my life,
your death and life will be
Je - sus Christ, my life,
death and life will be,
Christ, my life, my light, my
life will be my stay, will
24
28
my light,
my stay
my light,
my stay
life, my light,
be my stay
28
I
(II)

32
my guard,
when I
my guard,
when I
my
when
32
36
my must trust go by my day home -
my must trust go by day my home -
guard, I my must trust go by my
my when guard, I my must trust go by my
36

40
and
night:
ward
way;
and
night, my guard, my trust by day and
ward
way, when I must go my home-ward
day and night, my guard by day and
home-ward way, must go my home - ward
day and night, my guard, my trust by day and
home - ward way, when I must go my home-ward
40
44
night:
way;
night:
way;
on
throw
night:
way;
44

48
on
throw
on earth I roam,__ a pass - ing
throw wide the heav'n - ly gate of
earth I roam,__ a pass - ing guest, pass -
wide the heav'n - ly gate of grace, gate______
48
II
52
earth I roam,________ a
wide the heav'n - ly
guest, pass - ing guest, on earth________ I roam, a pass -
grace, gate of grace, throw wide________ the heav'n - ly gate______
- ing guest, on earth________ I roam, a
______ of grace, throw wide________ the heav'n - ly
on earth I____ roam,__ a pass - ing
throw wide the____ heav'n - ly gate of
52
I
(II)

56
pass - ing guest;
gate of grace
- ing guest, on earth I roam, a pass - ing
of grace, throw wide the heav'n - ly gate of
pass - ing guest, a guest, on earth I
gate of grace, throw wide, throw wide the
guest, on earth I roam, a pass - ing
grace, throw wide the heav'n - ly gate of
56
60
guest, a pass - ing guest;
grace, heav'n - ly gate of grace
roam, I roam a pass - ing guest;
heav'n - ly gate, the gate of grace
guest, but a pass - ing guest;
grace, heav'n - ly gate of grace
60

64
68
Tenor
re - move sin's weight
when I have run
Bass
re - move sin's
when I have
68
II
72
Alto
re - move sin's
when I have
and send me rest, and send me
the faith - ful race, the faith - ful
weight and send me rest,
run the faith - ful race,
72

76
weight and send me
run the faith - ful
rest, re - move sin's weight and send me
race, when I have run the faith - ful
re - move sin's weight and send me
when I have run the faith - ful
76
79
Soprano
re - move sin's weight
when I have run
rest, re - move sin's weight and
race, when I have run the
rest, re - move sin's weight and send me rest,
race, when I have run the faith - ful race,
rest, re - move sin's weight and send me
race, when I have run the faith - ful
79
I
(II)

83
and send me rest.
the faith - ful race.
send me rest, re - move sin's weight and
faith - ful race, when I have run the
re - move sin's weight and send me rest,
when I have run the faith - ful race,
rest, re - move sin's weight and send
race, when I have run the faith -
83
87
D.S. al fine
send me rest, and send me rest.
faith - ful race, the faith - ful race.
and send me rest.
the faith - ful race.
me rest, and send me rest.
- ful race, the faith - ful race.
87
D.S. al fine

Alleluia

5

al - le - lu - ia, al - le - lu - ia, al - le -

ia, al - le - lu - ia, al - le - lu -

lu - ia, al - le - lu - ia, al - le -

Al - le - lu - ia, al - le - lu - ia,

5 (II)

I: 16', 8'

9
lu - ia, al - le - lu - ia, al -
ia, al - le - lu - ia, al - le - lu - ia, al - le -
lu - ia, al - le - lu - ia, al - le - lu - ia,
al - le - lu - ia, al - le - lu - ia, al - le -
9
13
- le - lu - ia, al - le - lu - ia,
lu - ia, al - le - lu - ia, al - le -
al - le - lu - ia, al - le - lu - ia, al - le - lu-
lu - ia, al - le - lu - ia,
13

18
al - le - lu - ia, al - le - lu - ia, al - le - lu -
- lu - ia, al - le - lu - ia, al - le - lu - ia, al -
ia, al - le - lu - ia, al - le - lu - ia,
al - le - lu - ia, al - le - lu - ia,
18
23
ia, al - le - lu - ia, al - le - lu -
- le - lu - ia, al - le - lu - ia, al - le - lu -
al - le - lu - ia, al - le - lu - ia, al - le - lu -
al - le - lu -
23

28
ia, al - le - lu - ia,
ia, al - le - lu - ia, al - le - lu - ia, al - le - lu -
ia, al - le - lu - ia, al -
ia, al - le -
28
(II)
II
I
33
al - le - lu - ia, al -
ia, al - le - lu - ia, al - le - lu - ia, al - le -
le - lu - ia, al - le - lu - ia,
lu - ia, al - le - lu - ia, al - le - lu -
33

38
le - lu - ia, al - le - lu -
lu - ia, al - le - lu - ia,
al - le - lu - ia, al - le - lu - ia, al - le - lu - ia,
ia, al - le - lu - ia, al - le - lu -
38
43
ia, al - le - lu - ia,
al - le - lu - ia, al - le - lu -
al - le - lu - ia,
ia, al - le - lu - ia, al - le -
43

48
al - le - lu - ia, al - le - lu - ia, al - le -
ia, al - le - lu - ia, al - le - lu - ia, al - le -
al - le - lu - ia, al - le - lu - ia, al - le -
lu - ia, al - le - lu - ia, al - le - lu - ia, al -
48
53
lu - ia, al - le - lu - ia,
lu - ia, al - le - lu - ia, al - le - lu - ia,
lu - ia, al - le - lu - ia, al - le - lu - ia,
- le - lu - ia, al - le - lu - ia, al - le - lu - ia,
53

58
al - le - lu - ia, al - le - lu - ia, al - le -
al - le - lu - ia, al - le - lu - ia, al - le -
al - le - lu - ia, al - le - lu - ia, al - le -
al - le - lu - ia, al - le - lu - ia, al - le -
58
63
- lu - ia, al - le - lu - ia, al - le - lu - ia.
- lu - ia, al - le - lu - ia.
lu - ia, al - le - lu - ia.
lu - ia, al - le - lu - ia, al - le - lu - ia.
63

Jesu, Joy—My Joy Forever

Jesu bleibet meine Freude

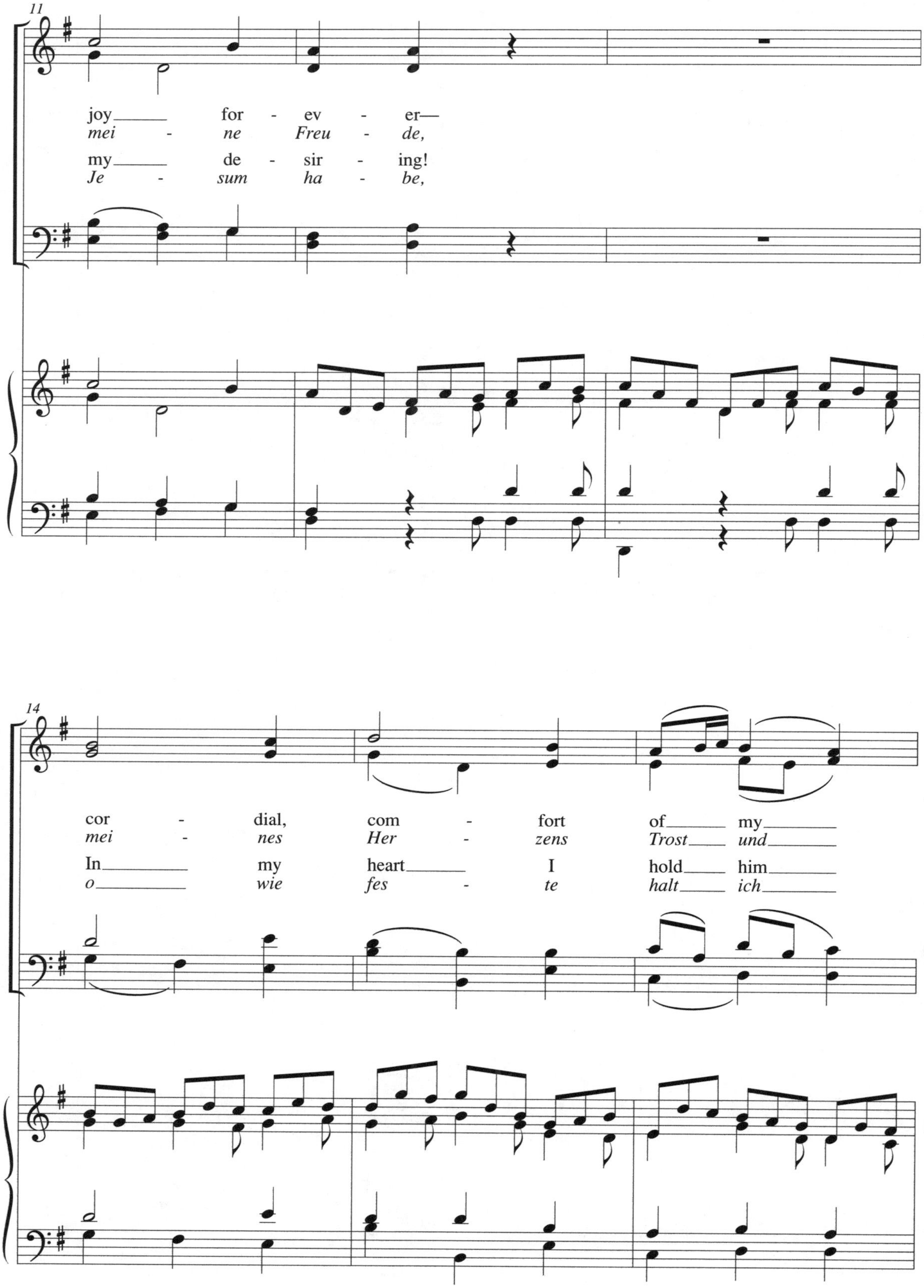

11

joy for - ev - er—
mei - ne Freu - de,

my de - sir - ing!
Je - sum ha - be,

17
soul,
Saft,
fast.
ihn,
20
23
Je - sus turns a -
Je - sus weh - ret
Je - sus comes with
daß er mir mein

27
way all sor - rows
al - lem Lei - de,
grace un - tir - ing
Her - ze la - be,

30
that would light and life con -
er ist mei - nes Le - bens
till all cares and grief are
wenn ich krank und trau - rig

33
trol.
Kraft,
past.
bin.
36
39
Strong
and
mei
-
ner
Well
I
Je
-
sum

42
righ - teous, Je - sus shin - ing,
Au - gen Lust und Son - ne,
know that Je - sus loves me,
hab ich, der mich lie - bet
45
bright - ness,
mei - ner
and his
und sich

48
plea - sure, good de - fin - ing,
See - le Schatz und Won - ne;
ver - y life he gives me.
mir zu ei - gen gi - bet;
51
so I
da - rum
Je - sus
ach drum

54
ev - er am a - ware,
laß ich Je - sum nicht
I will not for - sake,
laß ich Je - sum nicht,

57
heart and soul, of
aus dem Her - zen
though on earth my
wenn mir gleich mein

60
Je - sus there!
und Ge - sicht.
heart should break.
Her - ze bricht.
63
66
69

Now Thank We All Our God

Nun danket alle Gott

14
who won - drous things has
der gro - ße Din - ge
18
done,
tut
in
an
22
whom this world re - joi - ces;
uns und al - len En - den,

26
30
who, from our moth - ers' arms,
der uns von Mut - ter - leib
34
has
und

38
blest us on our way
Kin - des - bei - nen an
42
with
un -
46
count - less gifts of love,
zäh - lig viel zu gut,

50
and still is
und noch it -
54
ours to - day.
zund ge - tan.
58

Now Thank We All Our God

Nun danket alle Gott

What God Ordains Is Good Indeed

Was Gott tut, das ist wohlgetan

3

Soprano

What God or - dains is
Was Gott tut, das ist

Alto

What God or - dains is
Was Gott tut, das ist

Tenor

What God or - dains is
Was_ Gott tut, das ist

Bass

What God or - dains is
Was_ Gott tut,_ das ist

3

6
good in-deed. My friend will
wohl - ge-tan, da - bei will
good___ in-deed. My__ friend will
wohl - ge-tan, da - bei__ will
good_ in - deed. My friend will_
wohl - ge - tan, da - bei__ will_
good___ in-deed. My__ friend will_
wohl - ge-tan, da - bei will_
6
9
ne - ver fail me
ich ver - blei - ben.
ne - ver fail___ me
ich ver - blei - ben.
ne - ver__ fail______ me
ich__ ver - blei - ben.
ne - ver fail___ me
ich ver-blei - ben.
9

12
on dan - ger's path, in
Es mag mich auf die
on dan - ger's path, in
Es mag mich auf die
on__ dan - ger's path, in
Es__ mag mich auf die
on__ dan - ger's path, in
Es__ mag mich auf die
12
15
deep - est need, when death in
rau - he Bahn Not, Tod, und
deep - est need, when death in
rau - he Bahn Not,__ Tod,__ und
deep - est need, when death in__
rau - he Bahn Not, Tod,__ und_
deep - est need, when death in__
rau - he Bahn Not,__ Tod, und_
15

18
grief shall veil me.
E - lend trei - ben,
grief shall veil me.
E - lend trei - ben,
grief shall veil me.
E - lend trei - ben,
grief shall veil me.
E - lend trei - ben,
18
21
My God so dear, oh, draw me near; in lov - ing
so wird Gott mich ganz vä - ter - lich in sei - nen
My God so dear, oh, draw me near; in lov - ing
so wird Gott mich ganz vä - ter - lich in sei - nen
My God so dear, oh, draw me near; in lov - ing
so wird Gott mich ganz vä - ter - lich in sei - nen
My God so dear, oh, draw me near; in lov - ing
so wird Gott mich ganz vä - ter - lich in sei - nen
21

24
arms now hold me;
Ar - men hal - ten;
arms now hold me;
Ar - men hal - ten;
arms now hold me;
Ar - men hal - ten;
arms now hold me;
Ar - men hal - ten;
24
27
at last in light en - fold me.
drum laß ich ihn nur wal - ten.
at last in light en - fold me.
drum laß ich ihn nur wal - ten.
at last in light en - fold me.
drum laß ich ihn nur wal - ten.
at last in light en - fold me.
drum laß ich ihn nur wal - ten.
27
30

What God Ordains Is Good Indeed

Was Gott tut, das ist wohlgetan

Salvation unto Us Has Come

Es ist das Heil uns kommen her

All Who Believe and Are Baptized

Now All the Woods Are Sleeping

Nun ruhen alle Wälder

O Bread of Life from Heaven

Kyrie! God, Father in Heav'n Above

Kyrie, Gott Vater in Ewigkeit

7
things the mak - er and pre - serv -
Ding ein Schöp - fer und Re - gie -
things the mak - er and pre - serv -
Ding ein Schöp - fer und Re - gie -
things the mak - er and pre - serv -
Ding ein Schöp - fer und Re - gie -
things the mak - er and pre - serv -
Ding ein Schöp - fer und Re - gie -
7
9
er. E - le - i - son.
rer: e - le - i - son.
er. E - le - i - son.
rer: e - le - i - son.
er. E - le - i - son.
rer: e - le - i - son.
er. E - le - i - son.
rer: e - le - i - son.
9

12
Ky - ri - e! O Christ, our king,
Chri - ste al - ler Welt Trost,
Ky - ri - e! O Christ, our king,
Chri - ste al - ler Welt Trost,
Ky - ri - e! O Christ, our king,
Chri - ste al - ler Welt Trost,
Ky - ri - e! O Christ, our king,
Chri - ste al - ler Welt Trost,
12
15
sal - va - tion for all you came to
uns Sün - der al - lein du hast er -
sal - va - tion for all you came to
uns Sün - der al - lein du hast er -
sal - va - tion for all you came to
uns Sün - der al - lein du hast er -
sal - va - tion for all you came to
uns Sün - der al - lein du hast er -
15

17
bring. O Lord Je - sus, God's own Son, me - di -
löst. O Je - su Got - tes Sohn; un - ser
bring. O Lord Je - sus, God's own Son, me - di - a -
löst. O Je - su Got - tes Sohn; un - ser Mitt -
bring. O Lord Je - sus, God's own Son, me - di - a -
löst. O Je - su Got - tes Sohn; un - ser Mitt -
bring. O Lord Je - sus, God's own Son, me - di -
löst. O Je - su Got - tes Sohn; un - ser
17
20
a - tor for us at heav - en's throne: Hear our
Mitt - ler bist in dem höch - sten Thron, zu dir
- tor for us at heav - en's throne: Hear our
- ler bist in dem höch - sten Thron, zu dir
- tor for us at heav - en's throne: Hear our
- ler bist in dem höch - sten Thron, zu dir
a - tor for us at heav - en's throne: Hear our
Mitt - ler bist in dem höch - sten Thron, zu dir
20

23
cry and grant our sup - pli - ca -
schrei - en wir aus Her - zens - be -
cry and grant our sup - pli - ca -
schrei - en wir aus Her - zens - be -
cry and grant our sup - pli - ca -
schrei - en wir aus Her - zens - be -
cry and grant our sup - pli - ca -
schrei-en wir aus Her - zens - be -
23
25
tion. E - le - i - son.
gier: e - le - i - son.
tion. E - le - i - son.
gier: e - le - i - son.
tion. E - le - i - son.
gier: e - le - i - son.
tion. E - le - i - son.
gier: e - le - i - son.
25

28
Ky - ri - e! O God the Ho - ly Ghost, guard our
Ky - ri - e, Gott hei - li - ger Geist, tröst, stärk
Ky - ri - e! O God the__ Ho - ly Ghost, guard our__
Ky - ri - e, Gott hei - li - ger Geist, tröst, stärk_
Ky - ri - e! O God the__ Ho - ly____ Ghost, guard our
Ky - ri - e, Gott hei - li - ger____ Geist, tröst, stärk
Ky - ri - e! O__ God the__ Ho - ly__ Ghost, guard our__
Ky - ri - e, Gott hei - li - ger__ Geist, tröst, stärk
28
32
faith, the__ gift we need the most, and bless our life's last
uns im__ Glau - ben al - ler - meist, daß wir am letz - ten
__ faith, the gift we need__ the__ most, and bless our__ life's last
__ uns_ im Glau - ben al - ler - meist, daß wir__ am__ letz - ten
faith, the gift we___ need the most, and_ bless our life's_ last____
uns im Glau - ben___ al - ler - meist, daß_ wir__ am letz - ten____
faith, the gift we need________ the__ most, and_ bless our life's_______ last__
uns__ im Glau-ben al - ler - meist, daß_ wir am letz - ten__
32

35
hour, that we leave this sin - ful world with glad -
End fröh - lich ab - schei - den aus die - sem E -
hour, that we leave this sin - ful world with glad -
End fröh - lich ab - schei - den aus die - sem E -
hour, that we leave this sin - ful world with glad -
End fröh - lich ab - schei-den aus die - sem E -
hour, that we leave this sin-ful world with glad -
End fröh - lich ab - schei - den aus die - sem E -
35
38
ness. E - le - i - son.
lend: e - le - i - son.
ness. E - le - i - son.
lend: e - le - i - son.
ness. E - le - i - son.
lend: e - le - i - son.
ness. E - le - i - son.
lend: e - le - i - son.
38

All Glory Be to God on High

Allein Gott in der Höh sei Ehr

Soprano
Alto

Tenor
Bass

1 All glo - ry be to God on high; let thanks be sung for -
2 O Fa - ther, for your lord - ship true we give you praise and
3 Lord Je - sus Christ, the on - ly Son of God, cre - a - tion's
4 O Ho - ly Spir - it, per - fect gift, who brings us con - so -
Al - lein Gott in der Höh sei Ehr und Dank für sei - ne

4

ev - er! What - ev - er Sa - tan's host may try, God foils their grim en -
hon - or; we wor - ship you; we trust in you; we give you thanks for -
au - thor, re - deem - er of your wan - d'ring ones, and source of all true
la - tion: to men and wom - en saved by Christ as - sure your in - spi -
Gna - de, da - rum daß nun und nim - mer - mehr uns rüh - ren kann kein

8

deav - or. Our gra - cious God hears ev - 'ry call, gives
ev - er. Your will is per - fect, and your might re -
plea - sure: O Lamb of God, O Lord di - vine, con -
ra - tion. Through sick - ness, need, and bit - ter death, grant
Scha - de. Ein Wohl - ge - falln Gott an uns hat; nun

11

peace on earth, good - will to all, and calms the trou - bled spir - it.
lent - less - ly con - firms the right; your lord - ship is our bless - ing.
form our lives to your de - sign, and on us all have mer - cy.
us your warm, life - giv - ing breath; our lives are in your keep - ing.
ist groß Fried ohn Un - ter - laß, all Fehd hat nun ein En - de.

We All Believe in One True God

Wir glauben all an einen Gott

Soprano
Alto
Tenor
Bass
Keyboard
2 We all be - lieve, be - lieve in Je - sus Christ, his own Son, our Lord, pos -
2 Wir glau - ben auch an Je - sus Christ, sei - nen Sohn und un - sern
2 We all be - lieve in Je - sus Christ, his own Son, our Lord, pos -
2 Wir glau - ben auch an Je - sus Christ, sei - nen Sohn und un - sern
2 We all be - lieve in Je - sus Christ, his own Son, our Lord, pos -
2 Wir glau - ben auch an Je - sus Christ, sei - nen Sohn und un - sern
2 We all be - lieve in Je - sus Christ, his own Son, our Lord, pos -
2 Wir glau - ben auch an Je - sus Christ, sei - nen Sohn und un - sern

7
sess - ing an e - qual God - head, throne and
Her - ren, der e - wig bei dem Va - ter
sess - ing an e - qual God - head, throne
Her - ren, der e - wig bei dem Va -
sess - ing an e - qual God - head, throne and
Her - ren, der e - wig bei dem Va - ter
sess - ing an e - qual God - head, throne and
Her - ren, der e - wig bei dem Va - ter
7
10
might, source of ev - 'ry grace and bless - ing;
ist, glei - cher Gott von Macht und Eh - ren,
and might, source of ev - 'ry grace and bless - ing;
- ter ist, glei - cher Gott von Macht und Eh - ren,
might, source of ev - 'ry grace and bless - ing;
ist, glei - cher Gott von Macht und Eh - ren,
might, source of ev - 'ry grace and bless - ing;
ist, glei - cher Gott von Macht und Eh - ren,
10

13
born of Mar - y, vir - gin moth - er, by the
von Ma - ri - a, der Jung - frau - en, ist ein
born of Mar - y, vir - gin moth - er, by the
von Ma - ri - a, der Jung - frau - en, ist ein
born of Mar-y, vir - gin moth - er, by the
von Ma-ri-a, der Jung - frau - en, ist ein
born of Mar - y, vir - gin moth - er, by the pow -
von Ma - ri - a, der Jung - frau - en, ist ein wah -
13
16
pow - er of the Spir - it, Word made flesh, our
wah - rer Mensch ge - bo - ren durch den Heil - gen
pow - er of the Spir - it, Word made flesh,
wah - rer Mensch ge - bo - ren durch den Heil -
pow - er of the Spir - it, Word made flesh, our
wah - rer Mensch ge - bo - ren durch den Heil - gen
- er of the Spir - it, Word made flesh, our
- rer Mensch ge - bo - ren durch den Heil - gen
16

19
el - der broth - er; that the lost might
Geist im Glau - ben; für uns, die wir
our el - der broth - er; that the lost might
- gen Geist im Glau - ben; für uns, die wir
el - der broth - er; that the lost might
Geist im Glau - ben; für uns, die wir
el - der broth - er; that the lost might
Geist im Glau - ben; für uns, die wir
19
22
life in - her - it, was put
warn ver - lo - ren, am Kreuz ge -
life in - her - it, was put
warn ver - lo - ren, am Kreuz ge -
life in - her - it, was put
warn ver - lo - ren, am Kreuz
life in - her - it, was put
warn ver - lo - ren, am Kreuz
22

25

to death up - on the cross, the
stor - ben und vom Tod, vom

to death up - on the cross, the
stor - ben und vom Tod, vom

to death up - on the cross, the
ge - stor - ben und vom Tod, vom Tod, vom

to death up - on the cross, the
ge - stor - ben und vom Tod, vom Tod, vom

29

cross and raised by God vic - to - ri - ous.
Tod wie - der auf - er - stan - den durch Gott.

cross and raised by God vic - to - ri - ous.
Tod wie - der auf - er - stan - den durch Gott.

cross and raised by God vic - to - ri - ous.
Tod wie - der auf - er - stan - den durch Gott.

cross and raised by God vic - to - ri - ous.
Tod wie - der auf - er - stan - den durch Gott.

Holy, Holy, Holy

Sanctus

O Lamb of God Most Holy

O Lamm Gottes, unschuldig

Dona nobis pacem

6
cem, pa - cem,
pa - cem, do -
- cem, do - na no -
do - na no - bis,
6
8
do - na no - bis,
- na no - bis,
bis, do - na
do - na no -
8

10
do - na no -
do - na no - bis pa -
no - bis pa - cem, do - na no -
- bis pa - cem, do - na no - bis
10
12
- bis pa - cem, do - na no -
- cem, do - na no - bis,
bis, do - na
pa - cem,
12

14

bis, do -

do - na no -

no - bis pa - cem, pa -

pa - cem,

14

16

- na no - bis pa - cem,

- bis pa - cem, pa - cem, do -

cem, do - na no - bis pa -

do - na___ no - bis pa - cem,___

16

II

Ped./I

18

pa - cem, pa -

- na no - bis pa - cem,

- cem, pa - cem, do - na no - bis

do - na no -

18

(II)

I

Man.

20

- cem, do - na no -

pa - cem, pa - cem, do -

pa - cem, pa -

bis pa - cem,

20

II

22
bis pa - cem, do - na no - bis pa -
- na no - bis, do - na no - bis
- cem, do - na no -
pa - cem, do -
22
(II)
I
24
- cem, do - na no -
pa - cem, do - na
bis pa - cem, do - na no - bis, do -
- na no - bis, do - na no - bis
24

26
bis, do - na no - bis pa - cem,
no - bis pa - cem, pa - cem, do - na
- na no - bis pa - cem, pa - cem,
pa - cem, do -
26
II
Ped.
29
pa - cem, do - na no-bis pa - cem, do - na no -
no-bis do - na, pa - cem, do - na no - bis pa -
do - na no - bis pa - cem, do -
- na no - bis pa - cem, pa - cem, do -
29

32
- bis pa - cem, pa - cem,
- cem, pa - cem, do - na no -
- na no - bis pa - cem, do - na
- na no - bis pa - cem,
32
35
do - na no - bis pa - cem, pa -
- bis pa - cem, do - na pa -
no - bis pa - cem, do - na no - bis
do - na no - bis pa - cem,
35

38
cem, pa - cem, do -
- cem, do - na, do - na no -
pa - cem, do - na no - bis pa - cem, pa -
pa - cem, pa - cem, do -
38
(II)
I
Man.
40
- na,
bis pa - cem, do - na no - bis, do -
cem, do - na no - bis pa - cem,
-
-
40
Ped.

42
pa - cem, do -
- na no - bis pa -
do - na no - bis pa -
- na no - bis pa -
42
II
(Ped.)
44
- na, do - na no - bis_ pa - cem.
- cem, do - na no - bis pa - cem.
- cem, do - na___ no - bis pa - cem.
cem, do - na no - bis pa - cem.
44

Gloria in excelsis Deo

C Instrument

*Choral score is on p. 22.

"A Mighty Fortress Is Our God" ("Ein feste Burg ist unser Gott") from *Ein feste Burg ist unser Gott*, BWV 80. Tune: EIN FESTE BURG, Martin Luther (1483–1546). Text: Martin Luther (1483–1546); tr. *Lutheran Book of Worship*, © 1978.

"All Creatures Great and Small" ("Gelobet sei der Herr") from *Gelobet seist du, Jesu Christ*, BWV 94. Tune: O GOTT, DU FROMMER GOTT, Ahasuerus Fritsch (1629–1701). Text: Johann Olearius (ca. 1665); tr. Madeleine Forell Marshall (b. 1946), © Madeleine Forell Marshall.

"All Glory Be to God on High" ("Allein Gott in der Höh sei Ehr"), BWV 260. Tune: ALLEIN GOTT IN DER HÖH SEI EHR, Nikolaus Decius (ca. 1485–1546), based on plainsong Gloria, ca. 900. Text: Nikolaus Decius (ca. 1485–1546), st. 1–3; Joachim Slüter (1490–1532), st. 4; tr. Gilbert E. Doan (b. 1930), alt., © 1978 *Lutheran Book of Worship*.

"All Who Believe and Are Baptized." Setting from *Wahrlich, wahrlich, ich sage euch*, BWV 86. Tune: ES IST DAS HEIL UNS KOMMEN HER, *Etlich christlich Lieder*, Wittenberg, 1524, based on German hymn *Freu dich, du werthe Christenheit*, Mainz, ca. 1390. Text: Thomas H. Kingo (1634–1703); tr. George T. Rygh (1860–1943), alt.

"Alleluia" from *Lobet den Herrn alle Heiden* (Motet VI), BWV 230.

"Break Forth, O Beauteous Heavenly Light" ("Brich an, o schönes Morgenlicht") from *Christmas Oratorio*, BWV 248. Tune: ERMUNTRE DICH, MEIN SCHWACHER GEIST, Johann Schop (1590–1667). Text: Johann Rist (1607–1667); tr. John Troutbeck (1832–1899), st. 1; Arthur T. Russell (1806–1874), st. 2.

"Bring Low Our Ancient Adam" ("Ertöt uns durch dein Güte") from *Jesus nahm zu dich die Zwölfe*, BWV 22 and "Creator God Who Made Us" ("Du Schöpfer alle Dinge") from *Ihr, die ihr euch von Christo nennet*, BWV 164. Tune: HERR CHRIST, DER EINIG GOTTS SOHN, *Enchiridia*, Erfurt, 1524, based on German folksong "Mein Freud möcht sich wohl mehren," ca. 1400. Text: Elizabeth Cruciger (ca. 1500–1535); tr. Madeleine Forell Marshall (b. 1946), © Madeleine Forell Marshall. Alternate text "The Only Son from Heaven" ("Herr Christ, der einig Gotts Sohn) and "Awaken, Lord, Our Spirit" ("Laß uns in deiner Liebe"), Elizabeth Cruciger (ca. 1500–1535); tr. Arthur T. Russell (1806–1874).

"Christ Is Arisen" ("Christ ist erstanden"), BWV 276. Tune: CHRIST IST ERSTANDEN, Johann Klug, *Geistliche Lieder*, 1533, based on German hymn from Salzburg, ca. 1160, based on Latin sequence *Victimae paschali laudes*, attr. Wipo of Bergundy, ca. 1050. Text: German hymn based on Latin hymn *Surgit in hac die*, ca. 1100; tr. Martin L. Seltz (1909–1967), alt., © 1969 Concordia Publishing House.

"Christ Jesus Lay in Death's Strong Bands" ("Wir essen und leben wohl") from *Christ lag in Todesbanden*, BWV 4. Tune: CHRIST LAG IN TODESBANDEN, Johann Walter, *Geistliche Gesangbüchlein*, 1524, based on *Christ ist erstanden*. Text: Martin Luther (1483–1546); based on Latin sequence *Victimae paschali laudes* attr. Wipo of Burgundy, ca. 1050; tr. Richard Massie (1800–1887), alt.

"Come, Holy Ghost, God and Lord" ("Du heilige Brunst, süßer Trost") from *Der Geist hilft unser Schwachheit auf* (Motet II), BWV 226. Tune: KOMM, HEILIGER GEIST, HERRE GOTT, *Enchiridia*, Erfurt, 1524, based on German hymn from Ebersberg, ca. 1480. Text: German hymn from Ebersberg, ca. 1480, based on antiphon *Veni Sancte Spiritus*, ca. 1000, st. 1; Martin Luther (1483–1546), st. 2 and 3; tr. *The Lutheran Hymnal*, 1941, alt., based on Catherine Winkworth (1829–1878).

"Crucifixus" from *St. John Passion*, BWV 232. Text: Nicene Creed, ca. 325. Keyboard realization: Mark Bighley.

"Dona nobis pacem" from Mass in B Minor, BWV 232. Subject derived from plainsong *Gloria* and *Agnus Dei*, ca. 1500. Text: Latin mass, ca. 700. Keyboard realization: Frank Stoldt.

"From Heaven Above to Earth I Come" ("Vom Himmel hoch, da komm ich her") from *Magnificat*, BWV 243a. Tune: VOM HIMMEL HOCH, Martin Luther (1483–1546), based on folk melody, ca. 1400. Text: Martin Luther (1483–1546); tr. *Lutheran Book of Worship*, © 1978, based on Catherine Winkworth (1829–1878). Keyboard realization: Richard Erickson.

"From Heaven Above to Earth I Come" ("Ach mein herzliebes Jesulein") from *Christmas Oratorio*, BWV 248. Tune: VOM HIMMEL HOCH, Martin Luther (1483–1546), based on folk melody, ca. 1400. Text: Martin Luther (1483–1546); tr. *Lutheran Book of Worship*, © 1978, based on Catherine Winkworth (1829–1878).

"Gloria in excelsis Deo" from *Magnificat*, BWV 243a. Text: Latin hymn, ca. 700. Keyboard realization: Richard Erickson.

"Holy, Holy, Holy" ("Sanctus"). BWV 325. Tune: Plainsong, ca. 1100. Text: Latin acclamation, ca. 400; tr. International Consultation on English Texts, 1975, alt.

"Jesu, Joy—My Joy Forever" ("Jesus bleibet meine Freude") from *Herz und Mund und Tat und Leben*, BWV 147. Tune: WERDE MUNTER, MEIN GEMÜTE, Johann Schop (ca. 1590–1667). Text: Martin Jahn, ca. 1661; tr. Madeleine Forell Marshall (b. 1946), © 1999 Augsburg Fortress. Keyboard realization: Richard Erickson.

"Jesu, Joy of My Desiring" ("Wohl mir, daß ich Jesum habe") from *Herz und Mund und Tat und Leben*, BWV 147. Tune: WERDE MUNTER, MEIN GEMÜTE, Johann Schop (ca. 1590–1667). Text: Martin Jahn, ca. 1661; tr. Martin A. Seltz (b. 1951), © 1999 Augsburg Fortress. Keyboard realization: Richard Erickson.

"Jesus, My Sweet Pleasure" ("Jesu, meine Freude") from *Jesu, meine Freude* (Motet III), BWV 227. Tune:

JESU, MEINE FREUDE, Johann Crüger (1598–1662). Text: Johann Franck (1618–1677); tr. Madeleine Forell Marshall (b. 1946), © Madeleine Forell Marshall.

"Kyrie! God, Father in Heaven Above" ("Kyrie, Gott Vater in Ewigkeit"), BWV 371. Tune: KYRIE, GOTT VATER IN EWIGKEIT, German hymn, ca. 1537; adapted from plainsong *Kyrie fons bonitatis*, ca. 950. Text: Latin hymn, ca. 1100; tr. William Gustave Polack (1890–1950), alt.

"Lord Jesus Christ, God's Only Son" ("Jesus Christus, Gottes Sohn") from *Christ lag in Todesbanden*, BWV 4. Tune: CHRIST LAG IN TODESBANDEN, Johann Walter, *Geistliche Gesangbüchlein*, 1524, based on *Christ ist erstanden*. Text: Martin Luther (1483–1546); based on Latin sequence *Victimae paschali laudes* attr. Wipo of Burgundy, ca. 1050; tr. Martin A. Seltz (b. 1951), © 1999 Augsburg Fortress.

"Lord, Keep Us Steadfast in Your Word" ("Erhalt uns, Herr bei deinem Wort"). Setting from *Bleib bei uns, denn es will Abend werden*, BWV 6. Tune: ERHALT UNS, HERR, *Geistliche Lieder*, Wittenberg, 1543; attr. Martin Luther (1483–1546); based on Latin hymn, *Veni Redemptor gentium*, ca. 1100. Text: Martin Luther (1483–1546); tr. Catherine Winkworth (1829–1878), alt.

"Lord, Thee I Love with All My Heart" ("Ach Herr laß dein lieb Engelein") from *St. John Passion*, BWV 245. Tune: HERZLICH LIEB HAB ICH DICH, O HERR, anonymous in Bernard Schmid, *Zwei Bücher einer neuen Künstlichen Tabulatur auff Orgel und Instrument*, Strassburg, 1577. Text: Martin Schalling (1532–1608); tr. Catherine Winkworth (1829–1878), alt.

"Now All the Woods Are Sleeping" ("Nun ruhen alle Wälder"). Setting from *St. Matthew Passion*, BWV 244. Tune: O WELT, ICH MUß DICH LASSEN, Heinrich Isaac (ca. 1450–1517), based on folk melody, ca. 1400. Text: Paul Gerhardt (1607–1676); tr. *Lutheran Book of Worship*, © 1978, based on Catherine Winkworth (1829–1878).

"Now Thank We All Our God" ("Nun danket alle Gott") from *Gott der Herr ist Sonn und Schild*, BWV 79. Tune: NUN DANKET ALLE GOTT, Johann Crüger (1598–1662). Text: Martin Rinkhart (1586–1649); tr. Catherine Winkworth (1829–1878), alt. Keyboard realization: Mark Bighley.

"Now Thank We All Our God" ("Nun danket alle Gott"), BWV 386. Tune: NUN DANKET ALLE GOTT, Johann Crüger (1598–1662). Text: Martin Rinkhart (1586–1649); tr. Catherine Winkworth (1829–1878), alt.

"O Bread of Life from Heaven." Setting from *St. Matthew Passion*, BWV 244. Tune: O WELT, ICH MUß DICH LASSEN, Heinrich Isaac (ca. 1450–1517), based on folk melody, ca. 1400. Text: Latin hymn, ca. 1661; tr. *Lutheran Book of Worship*, © 1978, based on Philip Schaff (1819–1893) and Hugh Thomas Henry (1862–1946).

"O Jesus Christ, My Life, My Light" ("O Jesu Christ, meins Lebens Licht"), BWV 118. Tune: HERR JESU CHRIST, MEINS LEBENS LICHT, Johannes Eccard (1553–1611), based on German folksong *Ich fahr dahin*, ca. 1450. Text: attr. Martin Behm (1557–1622); tr. Martin A. Seltz (b. 1951), © 1999 Augsburg Fortress. Keyboard realization: Richard Erickson.

"O Lamb of God Most Holy" ("O Lamm Gottes, unschuldig"), BWV 401. Tune: O LAMM GOTTES, UNSCHULDIG, Nikolaus Decius (ca. 1485–1546), based on plainsong *Sanctus*, ca. 1200. Text: Nikolaus Decius (ca. 1485–1546), based on Latin hymn *Agnus Dei*, ca. 900; tr. Martin A. Seltz (b. 1951), © 1999 Augsburg Fortress.

"O Morning Star, How Fair and Bright!" ("Wie bin ich doch so herzlich froh") from *Wie schön leuchtet der Morgenstern*, BWV 1. Tune: WIE SCHÖN LEUCHTET DER MORGENSTERN, Philipp Nicolai (1556–1608). Text: Philipp Nicolai (1556–1608); tr. *Lutheran Book of Worship*, © 1978.

"O Sacred Head, Now Wounded" ("O Haupt voll Blut und Wunden") from *St. Matthew Passion*, BWV 244. Tune: HERZLICH TUT MICH VERLANGEN, Hans Leo Hassler (1564–1612), based on medieval secular song "Mein Gmüt ist mir verwirret," ca. 1500. Text: Paul Gerhardt (1607–1676), based on Arnulf of Louvain (ca. 1250); tr. James Waddell Alexander (1804–1859), alt.

"Salvation unto Us Has Come" ("Es ist das Heil uns kommen her"). Setting from *Wahrlich, wahrlich, ich sage euch*, BWV 86. Tune: ES IST DAS HEIL UNS KOMMEN HER, *Etlich christlich Lieder*, Wittenberg, 1524; based on German hymn *Freu dich, du werthe Christenheit*, Mainz, ca. 1390. Text: Paul Speratus (1481–1551); tr. *The Lutheran Hymnal*, 1941, alt.

"Savior of the Nations, Come" ("Nun komm, der Heiden Heiland") from *Nun komm, der Heiden Heiland*, BWV 61. Tune: NUN KOMM, DER HEIDEN HEILAND, *Enchiridia*, Erfurt, 1524, based on plainsong from Einsiedeln, ca. 1100. Text: Martin Luther (1483–1546), based on Latin hymn *Veni Redemptor gentium* attr. Ambrose of Milan (340–397); tr. William Reynolds (1816–1876), alt. Keyboard realization: Mark Bighley.

"Savior of the Nations, Come" ("Lob sei Gott dem Vater g'tan") from *Schwingt freudig euch empor*, BWV 36. Tune: NUN KOMM, DER HEIDEN HEILAND, *Enchiridia*, Erfurt, 1524, based on plainsong from Einsiedeln, ca. 1100. Text: Martin Luther (1483–1546), based on Latin hymn *Veni Redemptor gentium* attr. Ambrose of Milan (340–397); tr. William Reynolds (1816–1876), alt.

"Transcendent, Holy God" ("Dem wir das Heilig itzt") from *Gelobet sei der Herr, mein Gott*, BWV 129. Tune: O GOTT, DU FROMMER GOTT, Ahasuerus Fritsch (1629–1701). Text: Johann Olearius (1611–1684); tr. Madeleine Forell Marshall (b. 1946), © Madeleine Forell Marshall. Keyboard realization: Mark Bighley.

"Wake, Awake, for Night Is Flying" ("Gloria sei dir gesungen") from *Wachet auf, ruft uns die Stimme*, BWV 140. Tune: WACHET AUF, RUFT UNS DIE STIMME, Philipp Nicolai (1556–1608). Text: Philipp Nicolai (1556–

1608); tr. Martin A. Seltz (b. 1951), © 1999 Augsburg Fortress, based on Catherine Winkworth (1829–1878).

"We All Believe in One True God" ("Wir glauben all an einen Gott"), BWV 437. Tune: WIR GLAUBEN ALL AN EINEN GOTT, Wittenberg, 1524, based on German hymn, ca. 1400, based on Latin *Credo*, ca. 1300. Text: Martin Luther (1483–1546), based on medieval hymn, ca. 1417; tr. *The Lutheran Hymnal*, 1941.

"What God Ordains Is Good Indeed" ("Was Gott tut, das ist wohlgetan") from *Die Elenden sollen essen*, BWV 75. Tune: WAS GOTT TUT, DAS IST WOHLGETAN, Severus Gastorius (ca. 1650). Text: Samuel Rodigast (1649–1708); tr. Martin A. Seltz (b. 1951), © 1999 Augsburg Fortress.

"What God Ordains Is Good Indeed" ("Was Gott tut, das ist wohlgetan") from *Was Gott tut, das ist wohlgetan*, BWV 99. Tune: WAS GOTT TUT, DAS IST WOHLGETAN, Severus Gastorius (ca. 1650). Text: Samuel Rodigast (1649–1708); tr. Martin A. Seltz (b. 1951), © 1999 Augsburg Fortress.

"Zion Hears the Watchmen Singing" ("Zion hört die Wächter singen") from *Wachet auf, ruft uns die Stimme*, BWV 140. Tune: WACHET AUF, RUFT ZUNS DIE STIMME, Philipp Nicolai (1556–1608). Text: Philipp Nicolai (1556–1608); tr. Catherine Winkworth (1829–1878), alt. © 1999 Augsburg Fortress. Keyboard realization: Richard Erickson.

INDEXES

BACH-WERKE-VERZEICHNIS (BWV)

1 34
4 74, 79
6 82
22 37
36 1
61 2
75 118
79 112
80 83
86 124, 125
94 48
99 123
118 86
129 44
140 14, 16
147 103
164 37
226 80
227 49
230 96
232 62, 144
243a 22, 26
244 61, 126, 127
245 84
248 33, 36
260 135
276 69
325 141
371 128
386 117
401 143
437 136

BIBLICAL REFERENCES

PSALMS
18:1-3 84
28:2 128
46:1 83
100:4 112, 117
107:21-22 112, 117
122:6-7 144
139:11 126

ISAIAH
6:2-3 48
6:3 141
52:8 14
53:4-12 61
53:6-7 143
62:5-12 14

SIRACH
50:22-24 112, 117

MATTHEW
4:1-11 83
13:44-46 103
21:9 141
25:1-13 14, 16
27:29 61
27:32-37 62

MARK
16:6 69

LUKE
2:1-18 26, 33
2:14 22, 135
2:8-14 1, 2
4:1-13 83
16:22 84
17:13 128

JOHN
1:5, 14 1, 2
1:29 143
6:38-39 37, 44
6:48-51 127
8:31 82
11:25-27 136
14:16-18 80
14:27 144
16:13 80
19:16-18 62
20:19-23 144

ACTS
2:4 80
2:22-24 62
2:24 79

ROMANS
3:5 124
5:1-2 124
5:18-21 37
6:1-4 37
6:1-11 125
8:26-27 136
8:28-30 118, 123

1 CORINTHIANS
5:7 143
5:7-8 79
15:12-20 69
15:20-22 79
15:21 37
15:45-49, 55 37
15:51-57 74

2 CORINTHIANS
13:14 48

GALATIANS
3:16-21 124

EPHESIANS
2:20-22 118, 123

COLOSSIANS
2:12-13 125

1 TIMOTHY
2:5-6 128

2 TIMOTHY
1:10 79

TITUS
2:11-13 33
3:4-7 128

HEBREWS
1:1-8 136
13:8 34

1 PETER
1:18-19 103, 143

1 JOHN
4:9 37, 44
5:4-9 135

REVELATION
22:20 1, 2
21:21-23 14
22:16 34

TOPICAL

ADVENT
Savior of the Nations, Come, 2
Savior of the Nations, Come (chorale), 1
Wake, Awake for Night is Flying (chorale), 14
Zion Hears the Watchmen Singing, 16

CHRISTMAS
Break Forth, O Beauteous Heavenly Light (chorale), 36
From Heaven Above to Earth I Come, 26
From Heaven Above to Earth I Come (chorale), 33
Gloria in excelsis Deo, 22

NEW YEAR
From Heaven Above to Earth I Come (chorale), 33
O Morning Star, How Fair and Bright! (chorale), 34

EPIPHANY
O Jesus Christ, My Life, My Light, 86
O Morning Star, How Fair and Bright! (chorale), 34
The Only Son from Heaven, 37

BAPTISM OF OUR LORD
The Only Son from Heaven, 37

TRANSFIGURATION
Jesu, Joy—My Joy Forever, 103
O Morning Star, How Fair and Bright! (chorale), 34
The Only Son from Heaven, 37
Transcendent, Holy God, 44

ASH WEDNESDAY
Bring Low Our Ancient Adam, 37

LENT
A Mighty Fortress Is Our God (chorale), 83
Bring Low Our Ancient Adam, 37
Jesu, Joy of My Desiring, 103
Jesus, My Sweet Pleasure (chorales), 49
Kyrie! God, Father in Heaven Above, 128
Lord, Thee I Love with All My Heart (chorale), 84
O Jesus Christ, My Life, My Light, 86

SUNDAY OF THE PASSION/PALM SUNDAY/
GOOD FRIDAY
Crucifixus, 62
O Lamb of God Most Holy (chorale), 143
O Sacred Head, Now Wounded (chorale), 61

EASTER
All Who Believe and Are Baptized (chorale), 125
Alleluia, 96
Christ Is Arisen, 69
Christ Jesus Lay in Death's Strong Bands (chorale), 79
Lord Jesus Christ, God's Only Son, 74

PENTECOST
Come, Holy Ghost, God and Lord (chorale), 80

HOLY TRINITY
All Creatures Great and Small (chorale), 48
All Glory Be to God on High (chorale), 135
Transcendent, Holy God, 44
We All Believe in One True God (chorale), 136

REFORMATION
A Mighty Fortress Is Our God (chorale), 83
Lord, Keep Us Steadfast in Your Word (chorale), 82
Salvation unto Us Has Come (chorale), 124

ALL SAINTS/END TIMES/NOVEMBER
Lord, Thee I Love with All My Heart (chorale), 84
Now All the Woods Are Sleeping, 126
O Jesus Christ, My Life, My Light, 86
Wake, Awake, for Night Is Flying (chorale), 14
Zion Hears the Watchmen Singing, 16

CHRIST THE KING
O Morning Star, How Fair and Bright! (chorale), 34
Transcendent, Holy God, 44

BAPTISM
All Who Believe and Are Baptized (chorale), 125
Bring Low Our Ancient Adam, 37

COMMUNION
All Creatures Great and Small (chorale), 48
Christ Jesus Lay in Death's Strong Bands (chorale), 79
O Bread of Life from Heaven (chorale), 127
Wake, Awake, for Night Is Flying (chorale), 14

EVENING
Now All the Woods Are Sleeping, 126

WEDDING
Jesu, Joy of My Desiring, 103
Now Thank We All Our God, 112
Now Thank We All Our God (chorale), 117
O Morning Star, How Fair and Bright! (chorale), 34

FUNERAL
Lord, Thee I Love with All My Heart (chorale), 84
O Jesus Christ, My Life, My Light, 86
O Morning Star, How Fair and Bright! (chorale), 34
What God Ordains Is Good Indeed, 118
What God Ordains Is Good Indeed (chorale), 123

LITURGICAL
Kyrie! God, Father in Heaven Above, 128
All Glory Be to God on High, 135
Gloria in excelsis Deo, 22
Alleluia, 96
We All Believe in One True God, 136
Holy, Holy, Holy, 142
O Lamb of God Most Holy, 143

STEWARDSHIP/THANKSGIVING
Now Thank We All Our God, 112
Now Thank We All Our God (chorale), 117

GENERAL
Alleluia, 96
Jesu, Joy—My Joy Forever, 103
Jesu, Joy of My Desiring, 103
Now Thank We All Our God, 112
Now Thank We All Our God (chorale), 117
Salvation unto Us Has Come (chorale), 124
What God Ordains Is Good Indeed, 118
What God Ordains Is Good Indeed (chorale), 123

TUNE

ALLEIN GOTT IN DER HÖH SEI EHR, 135
CHRIST IST ERSTANDEN, 69
CHRIST LAG IN TODESBANDEN, 74, 79
EIN FESTE BURG IST UNSER GOTT, 83
ERHALT UNS, HERR, 82
ERMUNTRE DICH, MEIN SCHWACHER GEIST, 36
ES IST DAS HEIL UNS KOMMEN HER, 124, 125
HERR CHRIST, DER EINIG GOTTS SOHN, 37
HERR JESU CHRIST, MEINS LEBENS LICHT, 86
HERZLICH LIEB HAB ICH DICH, O HERR, 84
HERZLICH TUT MICH VERLANGEN, 61
JESU, MEINE FREUDE, 49
KOMM, HEILIGER GEIST, HERRE GOTT, 80
KYRIE, GOTT VATER IN EWIGKEIT, 128
NUN DANKET ALLE GOTT, 112, 117
NUN KOMM, DER HEIDEN HEILAND, 1, 2
O GOTT, DU FROMMER GOTT, 44, 48
O LAMM GOTTES, UNSCHULDIG, 143
O WELT, ICH MUß DICH LASSEN, 126, 127
VOM HIMMEL HOCH, 26, 33
WACHET AUF, RUFT UNS DIE STIMME, 14, 16
WAS GOTT TUT, DAS IST WOHLGETAN, 118, 123
WERDE MUNTER, MEIN GEMÜTE, 103
WIE SCHÖN LEUCHTET DER MORGENSTERN, 34
WIR GLAUBEN ALL AN EINEN GOTT, 136

TUNE SOURCES

Anonymous in Bernard Schmid, *Zwei Bücher einer neuen Künstlichen Tabulatur auff Orgel und Instrument, Strassburg*, 84
Crüger, Johann, 49, 112, 117
Decius, Nikolaus, 135, 143
Eccard, Johannes, 86
Enchiridia, Erfurt, 1, 2, 37, 80
Etlich christlich Lieder, Wittenberg, 124, 125
Fritsch, Ahasuerus, 44, 48
Gastorius, Severus, 118, 123
Geistliche Lieder, Wittenberg, 82
German folksong, 26, 33, 37, 86, 126, 127
German hymn, 69, 80, 124, 125, 128, 136
Hassler, Hans Leo, 61
Isaac, Heinrich, 126, 127
Klug, Johann, *Geistliche Lieder* (1533), 69
Latin hymn, 82
Luther, Martin, 26, 33, 83
Nicolai, Philipp, 14, 16, 34
Plainsong, 1, 2, 128, 135, 141, 142, 143, (144)
Schop, Johann, 36, 103
Walter, Johann, *Geistliche Gesangbüchlein* (1524), 74, 79
Wittenberg (1524), 136

TEXT SOURCES

Behm, Martin, 86
Cruciger, Elizabeth, 37
Decius, Nikolaus, 135, 143
Franck, Johann, 49
Gerhardt, Paul, 61, 126
German hymn, 69, 80
Jahn, Martin, 103
Kingo, Thomas H., 125
Latin acclamation, 141
Latin hymn, 22, 127, 128, 144
Latin sequence, 69, 74, 79, 80
Luther, Martin, 1, 2, 26, 33, 74, 79, 80, 82, 83, 136

Medieval hymn, 136
Nicene Creed, 62
Nicolai, Philipp, 14, 16, 34
Olearius, Johann, 44, 48
Rinkhart, Martin, 112, 117
Rist, Johann, 36
Rodigast, Samuel, 118, 123
Schalling, Martin, 84
Slüter, Joachim, 135
Speratus, Paul, 124

TRANSLATIONS

Alexander, James Waddell, 61
Doan, Gilbert E., 135
Henry, Hugh Thomas, 127
International Consultation on English Texts, 142
Lutheran Book of Worship, 26, 33, 34, 83, 126
Marshall, Madeleine Forell, 37, 44, 48, 49, 103
Massie, Richard, 79
Polack, William Gustave, 128
Reynolds, William, 1, 2
Russell, Arthur T., 36, 37
Rygh, George T., 125
Schaaf, Philip, 127
Seltz, Martin A., 14, 74, 86, 103, 118, 123, 143
Seltz, Martin L., 1, 69
The Lutheran Hymnal, 80, 124, 136
Troutbeck, John, 36
Winkworth, Catherine, (14), 16, (26), (33), (80), 82, 84, 112, 117, (126)

TITLE

A Mighty Fortress Is Our God (chorale), 83
Ach Herr, laß dein lieb Engelein, 84
Ach mein herzliebes Jesulein, 33
All Creatures Great and Small (chorale), 48
All Glory Be to God on High (chorale), 135
All Who Believe and Are Baptized (chorale), 125
Allein Gott in der Höh sei Ehr, 135
Alleluia, 96
Break Forth, O Beauteous Heavenly Light (chorale), 36
Brich an, o schönes Morgenlicht, 36
Bring Low Our Ancient Adam, 37
Christ Is Arisen (chorale), 69
Christ ist erstanden, 69
Christ Jesus Lay in Death's Strong Bands (chorale), 79
Come, Holy Ghost, God and Lord (chorale), 80
Crucifixus, 62
Dem wir das Heilig itzt, 44
Dona nobis pacem, 144
Du heilige Brunst, süßer Trost, 80
Ein feste Burg ist unser Gott, 83
Erhalt uns, Herr, bei deinem Wort, 82
Ertöt uns durch dein Güte, 37
Es ist das Heil uns kommen her, 124
From Heaven Above to Earth I Come, 26
From Heaven Above to Earth I Come (chorale), 33
Gelobet sei der Herr, 48
Gloria in excelsis Deo, 22
Gloria sei dir gesungen, 14
Herr Christ, der einig Gotts Sohn, 37
Holy, Holy, Holy, 142
Jesu, Joy—My Joy Forever, 103
Jesu, Joy of My Desiring, 103
Jesu, meine Freude, 49
Jesus bleibet meine Freude, 103
Jesus Christus, Gottes Sohn, 74
Jesus, My Sweet Pleasure (chorales), 49
Kyrie! God, Father in Heaven Above, 128
Kyrie, Gott Vater in Ewigkeit, 128
Lord Jesus Christ, God's Only Son, 74
Lord, Keep Us Steadfast in Your Word (chorale), 82
Lord, Thee I Love with All My Heart (chorale), 84
Now All the Woods Are Sleeping (chorale), 126
Now Thank We All Our God, 112
Now Thank We All Our God (chorale), 117
Nun danket alle Gott, 112
Nun danket alle Gott (chorale), 117
Nun komm, der Heiden Heiland (chorale), 1
Nun komm, der Heiden Heiland, 2
Nun ruhen alle Wälder, 126
O Bread of Life from Heaven (chorale), 127
O Haupt voll Blut und Wunden, 61
O Jesu Christ, meins Lebens Licht, 86
O Jesus Christ, My Life, My Light, 86
O Lamb of God Most Holy (chorale), 143
O Lamm Gottes, unschuldig, 143
O Morning Star, How Fair and Bright! (chorale), 34
O Sacred Head, Now Wounded (chorale), 61
Salvation unto Us Has Come (chorale), 124
Sanctus, 142
Savior of the Nations, Come (chorale), 1
Savior of the Nations, Come, 2
The Only Son from Heaven, 37
Transcendent, Holy God, 44
Vom Himmel hoch, da komm ich her, 26
Wake, Awake, for Night Is Flying (chorale), 14
Was Gott tut, das ist wohlgetan, 118
Was Gott tut, das ist wohlgetan (chorale), 123
We All Believe in One True God, 136
What God Ordains Is Good Indeed, 118
What God Ordains Is Good Indeed (chorale), 123
Wie bin ich doch so herzlich froh, 34
Wir essen und leben wohl, 79
Wir glauben all an einen Gott, 136
Wohl mir, daß ich Jesum habe, 103
Zion Hears the Watchmen Singing, 16
Zion hört die Wächter singen, 16